TOM WRIGHT is the official club historian and
Historical Trust, a supporters-led initiative
preserve and promote the proud history of the club. Now in his 62nd
year of supporting the club, he is also the author of *The Golden Years:
Hibernian in the Days of the Famous Five*, *Hibernian: From Joe Baker
to Turnbull's Tornados*, *Leith: A Glimpse of Times Past*, *Hibernian:
The Life and Times of a Famous Football Club* and the co-author of
Crops: The Alex Cropley Story and *Hibs Through and Through: The
Eric Stevenson Story*.

The History of the Hibs Quiz Book

TOM WRIGHT

Luath Press Limited

EDINBURGH

www.luath.co.uk

First published 2018
Reprinted 2019, 2020

ISBN: 978-1-912147-81-6

The book is made of materials from well-managed, FSC®-certified
forests and other controlled sources.

Printed and bound by Ashford Colour Press, Gosport

Typeset in 11 point Sabon by Main Point Books, Edinburgh

Contents

ANSWERS

Introduction

THE GREAT IRISH Potato Famine of the mid-19th century, which also affected parts of Scotland, the south of England and northern Europe, led to a severe shortage of food and eventually mass starvation and death for many. In Ireland alone it is said that from a population of around eight million at that time, almost one million would die as a result of starvation and disease. The vast majority of the Irish population, particularly those in the rural areas, were the poor who depended on the potato as their staple diet, and with little or no food many were left with no option but to move elsewhere to survive. The fortunate few would make their way to America, some to Australia, but most would travel to nearby England and Scotland.

In 1875 a group of young Irishmen or descendants of Irishmen living in Edinburgh decided to start a football team, the eventual result the Hibernian Football Club that we all know so well today. From its humble beginnings in the Cowgate area of the city, after a difficult start the club would soon force its way to the very forefront of Scottish football, leading the way in many of the developments that would shape the game as we know it today.

In quiz form, this book highlights the fascinating journey of the football club throughout the past 142 years. Divided into 31 separate sections in chronological order from the early days to the present time, it provides an ideal opportunity, often in detail, to learn more about the history of one of Scotland's greatest football teams.

I IN THE BEGINNING

1 Why the name Hibernian?

2 Hibs first recorded game was on Christmas Day 1875. Where was the game played and who were the opponents?

3 The club was taken under the wing of which church organisation?

4 Why were the Hibs initially refused permission to join the Scottish Football Association?

5 Describe the Hibs players' jerseys before a change to all-green around 1879.

6 Where did the club hold its first monthly meetings?

7 Why, in the early days, was it imperative that Hibs find their own home ground?

8 Who was the first captain of Hibs, and what was his connection to the club captain during its centenary year in 1975?

9 Who was the first Hibs player to be capped at an international level?

10 It is generally accepted that Hibs have had five home grounds since 1875. Can you name them?

11 Who were the opponents in the club's first ever Scottish Cup tie and what was the score?

12 Although only indirectly involving Hibs, which World's first took place at the first Easter Road stadium in May 1881?

13 What was the significance of the Hibs game against Blackburn

Rovers at Ewood Park on 16 April 1881?

14 In 1878, one of Scotland's first-ever floodlit games took place in Edinburgh between Hibs and an Edinburgh select. Where was the game played?

15 The first silverware won by the club was the Edinburgh Association Cup in 1879. Who did Hibs beat in the final?

16 The Easter Road side would win the Edinburgh Association tournament every season between 1879 and 1887, except once in 1883. What were the controversial circumstances behind the result that year?

17 A record Hibs victory from 1881 stands to this day. Who were their opponents?

18 Why would an outing to Ayrshire in 1883 prove so beneficial to the club?

19 The father of which future Hibs manager was said to have been part of the Cowlairs side that faced Hibs in the game organised to officially open Celtic's first Parkhead ground in 1888?

20 Which player from the 1880s was so popular with the fans that he was nicknamed 'darling'?

2 THE EARLY YEARS

1 Why was Hibs' Scottish Cup tie against rivals Hearts at Powderhall in November 1879 postponed shortly before the kick-off?

2 Which Hibs captain of the 1880s later went on to manage Hearts?

3 Who were Hibs' opponents in the first game at the new Easter Road ground in 1880?

4 After winning the Edinburgh Association Cup for a third consecutive season, the club was allowed to retain the trophy in perpetuity. What replaced it?

5 Why was the Scottish Cup Final victory against Dumbarton in 1887 clouded in controversy?

6 Where did the Cup Final take place?

7 Why was victory in the 1887 Scottish Cup Final one of the factors that would eventually lead to the club temporarily going out of business in 1891?

8 Centre forward Jeremiah 'Gerry' Reynolds would miss the 1887 Scottish Cup Final because of injury, but in 1892 he would take part in which prominent Scottish side's first ever success in the competition?

9 In 1887, Hibs became the unofficial World Champions after defeating which English side?

10 Which former Hibs player was later said to have been the first to be transferred for more than £100?

11 In what year did Hibs move to the present stadium at Easter Road?

12 Why was the club denied promotion despite winning the inaugural Scottish Second Division in 1894?

13 In 1896, the kick-off for the Hibs game against Celtic at Parkhead was delayed and three of the Celtic players were later suspended by the club. What was the reason?

14 Hibs faced Hearts in the final of the Scottish Cup in 1896. Where was the game played and what was the significance of the occasion?

15 Why was Hibs' winning goal in the 1902 Scottish Cup Final against Celtic said to have been scored in controversial circumstances?

16 Why was the venue for the 1902 Cup Final changed at the last minute?

17 Only weeks after winning the Scottish Cup in 1902, Hibs defeated Celtic in another cup final. What was the name of this tournament and what was the score?

18 Which Hibs manager would later manage Arsenal?

19 In 1905, the club planned to move from Easter Road. Where did they intend to go?

20 Which Hibs player was badly injured in a game against Partick Thistle at Firhill in 1909 and died a few days later?

3   THE FIRST WORLD WAR

1   Name the only player from Hibs' 1902 Scottish Cup winning side still at the club by the outbreak of the First World War in 1914.

2   The captain of Hibs' Scottish Cup-winning side in 1902 and League Champions the following season would later lose his life during the First World War. Who was he?

3   Why would football players sometimes be handed white feathers in the street?

4   A future Hibs chairman, he enlisted in the McCrae's Battalion of the Royal Scots in 1914 but would soon be invalided out on health grounds. Who was he?

5   In April 1915 Hibs and Hearts would temporarily join forces for a game. What was the occasion?

6   Although not directly linked to the club, the future Hibs player Bobby Comb's father and two uncles were involved in what tragic rail accident in 1915 that would affect the whole of Leith and beyond?

7   For what purpose was Easter Road ground used by the military in the early years of the war?

8   The prolific Hibs goal scorer James Hendren died from natural causes during the war. He was related to which legendary Hibs player of the 1960s and '70s?

9   What change was made to the league structure in Scotland between the years 1915 and 1921?

10 How many sides were in the First Division during this time?

11 Which former Hibs player, who also fought in the Boer War, was killed at the Battle of the Somme on 14 July 1916?

12 Serving Hibs well throughout the war years, who was the only player to have played for the club in the 1914, 1923 and 1924 Scottish Cup finals?

13 Who was the Hibs manager during the First World War?

14 Who replaced him in the Easter Road hot seat?

15 Which player, who was born in Chicago, played for Hibs in the 1914 Scottish Cup Final and would be killed in action in November 1918?

16 Born on Islay, which future Hibs manager joined the club in the closing days of the First World War?

17 Which serving Hibs player throughout the conflict would be badly gassed while winning the Military Cross in 1918?

18 Hibs didn't fare particularly well during the First World War. What was their lowest finishing position in the league between the years 1915 and 1919?

19 Who won the Scottish Cup in 1917?

20 On 21 September a combined Hibs/Hearts XI played a Rangers/Celtic select at Tynecastle to raise funds for which well-known Edinburgh memorial?

4 HIBS AND THE SCOTTISH CUP

1   In what year was the Scottish Cup first played for?

2   Who were Hibs' opponents in the last Scottish Cup final before the First World War?

3   This player played against Hibs in the 1914 final and for Hibs in the 1923 final. What was his name?

4   Which wartime guest player at Easter Road would score the winning goal for Aberdeen against Hibs in the 1947 final?

5   Why did centre forward Jock Weir, who scored four of Hibs' goals in a comprehensive 8-0 victory over Alloa in the first round of the 1946–47 competition, miss the following week's game?

6   What took place for the very first time at the end of the 1947 Scottish Cup Final between Hibs and Aberdeen?

7   John Cuthbertson scored twice in the Hibs' 2-0 Scottish Cup first-round tie with Albion Rovers at Cliftonville in January 1948, but the result would pale into insignificance with what breaking news later that evening?

8   Hibs famously defeated Rangers 3-2 in the second round of the Scottish Cup at Ibrox in 1951. Who were the Hibs goal scorers that afternoon?

9   The Scottish Cup semi-final replay against Rangers at Hampden in 1958 would end in controversial circumstances. What was the reason?

10 Who would feature in the 1958 final because of injury to centre half John Paterson?

11 How many of the Famous Five played in the 1958 final against Clyde?

12 When Hearts defeated Hibs 2-1 in the second round of the Scottish Cup at Tynecastle in 1966, which Hibs player missed a penalty, his first miss from the spot since signing for the club in 1964?

13 Name the only Hibs player to play in both the 1972 and 1979 Scottish Cup finals.

14 Which former Celtic and Birmingham City player, then with Hibs, would make his last ever appearance in the 1972 Scottish Cup Final?

15 Which popular inside forward would miss the 1972 cup final after breaking his ankle in a game against Falkirk at Brockville?

16 Which is older, The FA Cup or Scottish Cup?

17 Who captained Hibs in the 2001 Scottish Cup Final against Celtic?

18 Who was sent off in the 2012 cup final against Hearts?

19 Including 2016, how many Scottish Cup Finals have Hibs appeared in since 1875?

20 After winning the cup in 2016, Hibs embarked on an extensive programme of visiting schools in the area with the trophy. During these visits the ribbons were not allowed to be shown on the cup. Why?

5   THE ROARING '20S

1   Who were the only players from Hibs' 1914 Scottish cup final team to feature regularly for the side during the 1920s?

2   What change was made to the league format in 1921?

3   The very first international game to be played at Wembley took place between England and Scotland in April 1924. Name the Hibs player who took part in the game.

4   In 1923 and 1924 Hibs reached consecutive Scottish Cup Finals, unfortunately losing both. Who were their opponents in both games?

5   Which full-back pairing served the club well for several years during the 1920s?

6   How many times in the decade between 1920 and 1930 did Hibs lose to Hearts in the New Year's Day game?

7   His uncharacteristic mistake is said to have cost Hibs the 1923 Scottish Cup Final. Who was he?

8   Where did the 1924 Scottish Cup Final against Airdrie take place?

9   In what year was the Easter Road Grandstand moved from the east side of the ground to the west?

10 Where did Hibs play some of their home games while the new stand was being built?

11 What change was made to the offside ruling in 1925?

12 Which goalkeeper temporarily replaced Willie Harper in the Scotland side and later permanently on the Hibs team?

13 The transfer of which player to Hearts in 1926 would create the same furore among the Hibs supporters as did Gordon Smith's move to Tynecastle 33 years later?

14 In 1928, which Hibs player became a Wizard at Wembley?

15 Jimmy McColl, who served the club for 50 years and was the first player to score 100 goals for Hibs, had a brief spell as manager of which Irish side?

16 In the late 1920s, which two Scottish international Hibs players would join Everton within weeks of each other?

17 Why was 19 January 1929 a bad day for Edinburgh football?

18 What made the result of Ayr's home game against Kilmarnock on Wednesday 29 April 1931 significant for Hibs?

19 Which three Hibs players from the 1920s would eventually go on to manage the side?

20 Apart from the earlier loss of several first team players, what was said to have been one of the main reasons for the club's relegation at the end of the 1930–31 season?

6   THE INTERNATIONAL GAME

1   Who was the first Hibs player to score a goal for Scotland?

2   Who was the first Hibs player to be capped by a country other than Scotland?

3   In a game against Belgium in 1951, Lawrie Reilly became Hibs most capped player. Who held the record before him?

4   Lawrie Reilly holds the record for the number of international caps won by a Hibs player while still at the club. Who is second?

5   Which Hibs full-back scored on his debut for Scotland against Wales in October 1948 in what would turn out to be his only international appearance?

6   Who was the first Hibs player to score a hat trick for Scotland and against which country?

7   How many full Scotland caps did Eddie Turnbull win?

8   Who was the first ever player from outside the Football League to be capped for the full England side?

9   Two players born in England made history when selected for Scotland's European Qualifier against Portugal at Hampden in 1971. The Arsenal goalkeeper Bob Wilson was one. Who was the other?

10   The Scotland manager Tommy Docherty once declared Hibs' Pat Stanton to be better than which famous English International?

11   Who replaced the injured Hibs player Alex Cropley during Scotland's game against Belgium at Hampden in 1971 to win his first full cap?

12 Joe Baker was capped by both Scotland and England. How did this happen?

13 What was the connection between the Scottish international players Alex Cropley of Hibs and Bruce Rioch of Derby County?

14 Which famous Hibs player's older brother was capped by the United States?

15 Which Hibs player lined up at inside left in Scotland's famous 1-0 victory over Italy in a World Cup qualifying match at Hampden in 1965?

16 Who won his first full Scotland cap as an 18-year-old against Brazil at Hampden in 1966?

17 How many of his 21 full Scotland caps did Colin Stein win while with Hibs?

18 Which Hibs full-back made his only international appearance for Scotland against the country of his father's birth in 1974?

19 Which player would win three of his four full Scotland caps playing against the same side, but only one while at Hibs?

20 Who scored a goal from a free kick against Saudi Arabia in Riyadh on his Scotland debut in 1988?

7 A NEW BEGINNING

1 On 5 September 1931, the Hibs goalkeeper George Blyth broke his leg in a home game against St Bernard's. On the same afternoon, which far more serious incident involving a goalkeeper was taking place at Ibrox during a game against Celtic?

2 Harry Swan first became a director of the club in 1931. Why was Swan's election to the board a first for the club?

3 Swan would resign at the end of his first season as a director of the club. What reason did he give for his resignation?

4 Where did the 1931–32 New Year's Day derby take place?

5 Why was Harry Swan initially unpopular with publicans in the area when he first became chairman?

6 Hugh McFarlane spent nine seasons at Easter Road in the 1920s and '30s. He was related to which Canadian born defender who played for the club in the early 2000s?

7 How many Edinburgh clubs were in the Second Division during the 1931–32 season?

8 The father of which Hearts player, who played against Hibs in the 7-0 game at Tynecastle in 1973, was a registered player at Easter Road during the 1932–33 season?

9 A long serving director of the club, who ran a public house in the vicinity of the stadium?

10 At the start of the 1933–34 season, what change was made to the Hibs jerseys?

11 A disastrous afternoon at Tynecastle in September 1935 would

soon lead to which two international players leaving club?

12 Signed from junior side Bo'ness Cadora during the 1936–37 season, he would go on to give the club 12 years loyal service and have an early influence on Gordon Smith. Who was he?

13 What were the unusual circumstances leading to Hibs signing Arthur Milne at the start of the 1937–38 season?

14 The result of which Scottish Cup game in 1938 would turn out to be a huge embarrassment for the club and its supporters?

15 Gerry Mayes signed for Hibs in time for the 1938–39 season. Later as a Dunfermline player, he would have an indirect part to play in the coming together of the Famous Five. What was the reason?

16 In what year did Hibs first introduce the white sleeves on their jerseys?

17 In 1939 Hibs reached the semi-finals of the Scottish Cup only to lose to the eventual winners Clyde. Which future Hibs goalkeeper was playing against the Easter Road side that afternoon?

18 The impeccably dressed and flamboyant Hibs manager Willie McCartney was said to have been rarely seen in public without what item?

19 The 1930s had proved to be a difficult time for the club. What was Hibs' highest finishing position in the First Division during the decade?

20 On 12 May 1937, an Edinburgh Select took on a Glasgow Select at Hampden to commemorate which national occasion?

8   BEHIND THE SCENES

1   Who was president of the club when Hibs won the Scottish Cup in 1902?

2   This long serving member of the Easter Road backroom staff scored more than a hundred goals for both Hibs and Celtic. Who was he?

3   Harry Swan made what many thought to be this rash promise soon after being elected chairman of the club in the 1933?

4   A well-known Hibs groundsman, he also helped run a well-known Edinburgh juvenile side and would recommend several players to the club?

5   Magnus Magnusson was given what task by the chairman in 1949?

6   What position did Harry Swan hold at the SFA between 1952–1956?

7   He made his debut in 1954 as understudy to Gordon Smith in a game against East Fife and would go on to give the club more than 12 years' loyal service, many as captain. Later returning to the club as coach under Eddie Turnbull he would be inducted into the Hibernian Hall of Fame in 2012. Who was he?

8   As well as Harry Swan, Hibs had two other directors during the golden post-war years. Who were they?

9   For what purpose were the premises at 7 Carlton Terrace in Edinburgh purchased in 1955?

10 Signed from Kirkintilloch Rob Roy in 1938, he later became trainer at Easter Road, a position specially created for him, before taking

up a similar position at Dundee in the late '50s. Who was he?

11 For several years in the 1950s, which volunteer organisation would be run at both Easter Road and Tynecastle?

12 A prominent Edinburgh businessman, who purchased the club from Harry Swan in 1963?

13 A popular physiotherapist/trainer, he joined Hibs from Third Lanark in 1963. Who was he?

14 Previously a trainer at Dunfermline, who was part of the deal that saw Jock Stein joining the club in 1964?

15 A former Motherwell player and later manager of St Mirren, name the individual who was part of Eddie Turnbull's backroom staff in the early 1970s.

16 For a short time in the early 1970s, Hibs trained at which sports complex in the west of the city?

17 A well-respected surgeon, he was president of the club during the early years of Tom Hart's tenure. Who was he?

18 This former player took charge of which recently resurrected Hibs third team in 1971?

19 In the 1970s there were rumours regarding which possible takeover of the club?

20 Which two former players became assistants to manager Pat Stanton in 1982?

9   THE SECOND WORLD WAR

1   How many league games had Hibs played in season 1939–40 before war was declared and football temporarily suspended?

2   Who would score Hibs last peacetime goal for six years?

3   Why was it more lucrative for guest players to play in Scotland rather than England during the Second World War?

4   What made the radio broadcast of the 1940 New Year's Day derby between Hibs and Hearts at Easter Road extremely unusual?

5   What was found to be missing immediately after the final whistle of the above 1940 New Year's Day game?

6   Why did Hibs threaten to go into voluntary liquidation in 1940?

7   Why did the signing of guest player Bob Hardisty initially create a problem for the club?

8   Which registered Everton player, who guested for Hibs between 1941 and 1946, had earlier been fined and suspended from the game because of financial irregularities?

9   Who were Hibs opponents in the inaugural Summer Cup final in 1941 and what was the score?

10 Bobby Combe scored four goals against this side in a wartime league game at Easter Road during season 1941–42?

11 With Scottish Football reverting to what was essentially part time football during the war, what was Gordon Smith's daytime employment during most of this time?

12 What made the final result of the Summer Cup final between Hibs and Rangers at Hampden in 1942 unusual?

13 Which registered Liverpool player, who would later became an extremely successful manager, won wartime Scotland caps as a guest player for Hibs during the years of conflict?

14 Hibs defeated Rangers in the final of the Southern League Cup at Hampden in 1944. What was unusual about the score?

15 The game against Aston Villa at Tynecastle in 1944 would be the start of what regular series of matches that would continue for several years?

16 What was significant about the entire Scottish forward line that played against England in the wartime international at Wembley on 14 October 1944?

17 Then a registered player with Preston North End, which future famous manager was a guest player for Partick Thistle against Hibs in the 1945 Summer Cup Final?

18 The father of the captain of Hibs Skol Cup winning side in 1991, who turned out as a guest player for the club during the war?

19 Who were Hibs opponents in their last game before the German surrender in May 1945 and what was the score?

20 Even after the German surrender in May 1945, the following season was still classed as an unofficial wartime campaign. Why?

10 GORDON SMITH

1   Although born in the Morningside area of Edinburgh, Smith would spend the majority of his young life in which Angus town?

2   He made two appearances for the Scottish Schoolboys side: against England and Ireland. Which future team mate, who would also make his Hibs debut on the same evening as Smith, was also in the Scotland side on both occasions?

3   From what junior club did Hibs sign the young Gordon Smith?

4   In 1941, the Hibs manager and chairman travelled from Edinburgh by train to sign the player at his home town. Why did the signing have to be completed elsewhere?

5   Name the manager who signed Smith for Hibs.

6   He made his Hibs debut in April 1941. Who were Hibs' opponents that evening and what was the score?

7   Smith made his international debut for Scotland in a wartime international in 1944. Who were the opponents, what was the score, and where was the game played?

8   This Rangers player was often considered to be Gordon Smith's main rival for a place in the Scotland side?

9   What individual goal scoring record did Smith equal in a game against Third Lanark at Easter Road in November 1947?

10 In the early 1950s he opened a roadhouse in the Willowbrae area of the city. What was it called?

11 How many competitive European appearances did Smith make for Hibs and how many goals did he score in those games?

12 Against which side did Smith score his 300th goal for the club?

13 In how many different positions did he feature in a full Scottish international?

14 What honour was bestowed on the player in a ceremony at the Waverley Market in Edinburgh in 1951?

15 How many managers did Gordon Smith play under at Hibs?

16 Against which side did he make his last ever appearance for Scotland?

17 Which Brazilian side were said to have been interested in signing the Hibs player?

18 How many goals did Gordon Smith score for the Easter Road club?

19 As well as a league championship medal in 1960, what other winner's medal did Smith collect during his time at Hearts?

20 He made football history by winning a league championship medal with three different clubs and none of them Celtic or Rangers. But with which side did he finally end his playing career?

11 THE FAMOUS FIVE

1 Eddie Turnbull made his first ever appearance for the Hibs first team against this side?

2 From what club was Willie Ormond signed?

3 The Famous Five made their very first competitive outing as a complete unit against what side in 1949?

4 All Five scored a hundred league goals or more for the club. Who was top goal scorer in the 1949–50 season?

5 Eddie Turnbull achieved what rare feat in a game against Celtic at Easter Road in January 1950?

6 Who was the only one of the Five to support Hibs as a youngster?

7 Turnbull won his third Scotland cap against Austria at Hampden in December 1950. What was significant about the result?

8 How many championship medals did the Five win collectively with Hibs?

9 How many of the Famous Five received a testimonial game?

10 What was the reason for Lawrie Reilly missing a large part of the 1953–54 season?

11 What was significant about Hibs home game against Clyde on 29 January 1955?

12 All of the Famous Five played for Scotland at full international level. Who was the last of the five to be capped?

13 How many times did the Famous Five feature as a complete unit

for Scotland?

14 Bobby Johnstone scored three goals against Queen of the South in a league game at Easter Road on 15 January 1955, why are they are not included in the official list of hat-tricks scored by a Hibs player?

15 Who replaced Johnstone in the Hibs forward line after his move to Manchester City in 1955?

16 How many Hibs players took part in the 1954 and 1958 World Cup Finals?

17 How many national cup finals did the famous five appear in as a complete unit?

18 He was the only one of the Five to play all his games for Scotland in the same position.

19 Who is Hibs' all-time top goal scorer in official competitive games?

20 In what order did the Famous Five players join the club and who was the last to leave?

12 BEHIND THE FIVE

1   Signed from Edinburgh Thistle on the very same day as Lawrie Reilly, which long serving Hibs player, who would win three league championship medals with the club, was originally an inside forward before moving back to wing half?

2   Who captained the club in both the 1947 Scottish Cup Final and the league championship success in 1948?

3   Goalkeeper Tommy Younger was signed from Hutchison Vale in 1948. At the juvenile side he would immediately follow this goalkeeper, who had also signed for Hibs, before going on to win an FA Cup winner's medal in 1953. Who was he?

4   Name the five Hibs players selected for Scotland against Belgium at Hampden in 1948.

5   What was fairly unusual about the Hibs half-back line of Buchanan, Paterson and Gallagher in the early 1950s?

6   Which team mates would form a full-back partnership for Scotland several times between 1947 and 1948?

7   An Irish international, who would win a championship medal with Hibs in 1951?

8   Which promising young defender broke his leg in a Scottish Cup semi-final against Motherwell at Tynecastle in 1951?

9   Who made his debut for the club when replacing the injured Gordon Smith in the game against Clyde at Easter Road in 1951 that gave Hibs the League title, and would later win a League Cup medal with Hearts in 1954?

10 Who was nicknamed 'Sailor' by his team mates on account of his

being torpedoed while serving aboard the destroyer HMS *Ghurkha* during the war?

11 Although born in Colchester, this Hibs player would win a Scottish League cap in 1952 when lining up against the Welsh League. His son would later play for Hibs before a move to Rangers. What was his name?

12 In seven seasons with the club, this Prestonpans born full-back would make just 17 league appearances for the side; three between 1946 and 1952 and 14 during the 1952–53 campaign. Who was he?

13 Which Hibs goalkeeper, who played a few games for the club during the 1952–53 season, had a son who would later gain fame in the 1970s and 1980s as a centre half for St Mirren, Leeds, Manchester United and Scotland?

14 Which 'Tiger' made his debut for the club against Aberdeen in 1954?

15 Which centre-half signed from Armadale Thistle in 1954 and would win one full cap for Scotland after his move to Manchester City in 1960?

16 This long-serving Hibs player would score eight goals in just six League Cup games at the start of the 1954–55 season, deputising for the incapacitated Lawrie Reilly. On Reilly's return a place in the side just had to be found for him and he was moved to inside left and later wing-half. What was his name?

17 Which future Hibs manager lined up at right-back in the home leg of Hibs European Cup game against Rot Weiss of Essen in 1955?

18 Although based in Germany with the Royal Scots, which goalkeeper rarely missed a Hibs game during his two years of National Service?

19 A member of the Scottish Cup final side that lost to Clyde in 1958 and capped twice for Scotland that same year, this player made his debut for the club during the 1954–55 season as an inside forward but would later form a well-established full-back pairing with Joe McClelland. What was his name?

20 Although still a registered Hibs player at the time, who scored the winning goal in Falkirk's replayed Scottish Cup Final victory against Kilmarnock in 1957?

13 LAWRIE REILLY

1 Lawrie Reilly joined Hibs from which well-known juvenile side?

2 As a schoolboy, he is said to have asked which Hibs footballer up to his house for tea after a game at Tynecastle?

3 Before he had even left school, the young Reilly had visited almost all the grounds in Scotland to watch Hibs. What made his travels to the away-grounds that much easier?

4 What was his occupation outside football before he became a full-time footballer at Easter Road?

5 In what position did Lawrie Reilly make his full Scotland debut?

6 Against which side did he score his first senior hat trick for Hibs?

7 What unusual circumstances made Reilly exempt from National Service?

8 How did he get the nickname 'Last Minute Reilly'?

9 How many goals did he score for the full Scotland side?

10 What is fairly unusual about the spelling of his Christian name?

11 After missing the start of the 1953–54 season Reilly made a goal scoring comeback against which well-known English side?

12 What was the reason behind him missing the return leg of the inaugural European Cup against Rot Weiss of Essen in 1955?

13 Where and when did he make his last appearance for Scotland?

14 What unique goal scoring record does he still hold in games

against England?

15 What is the most number of goals scored by Reilly in the one game for Hibs?

16 His last ever game was in April 1958. Who were the opponents and what was the score?

17 Against which side did Reilly become Hibs most capped player?

18 What was the reason for him almost missing Hibs game against Botafogo during the club's trip to South America in 1953?

19 He had a public house in Leith. What was it called?

20 Apart from supporting the club in his youth, what else made Lawrie Reilly different from the other members of the Famous Five?

14 THE LEAGUE CUP

1 Who were Hibs' opponents in its first ever league cup game in 1946?

2 In 1950, the Easter Road side topped their league cup section unbeaten without dropping a point but were only credited with winning five of the six games played. What was the reason?

3 Which member of the Famous Five scored a hat-trick in the 1950 semi-final against Queen of the South at Tynecastle?

4 Hibs defeated which team 6-2 away from home just two weeks before losing 3-0 to the same side in the 1950 League Cup Final?

5 Playing against Hibs in a league cup game at Easter Road in 1959, which player scored the fastest ever hat-trick in Scottish football?

6 In 1964, Hibs were defeated by this second division side at the semi-final stage of the competition?

7 What is the clubs highest ever score in a league cup game?

8 Who scored the winning goal in the last minute of the 1968 semi-final at Tynecastle with his leg heavily bandaged?

9 Why was the 1968 league cup final postponed until later in the season?

10 In the 1965–66 semi-final replay at Hampden, which Hibs' centre half was sent-off in a game against his former side Celtic?

11 What major changes were made to the league cup format in 1972?

12 This full-back scored the only goal of the game in the semi-final victory against Rangers in 1972?

13 Who were Hibs' first round opponents on their way to winning the Skol Cup in 1991, and what was fairly unusual about the venue?

14 In 1991, which Hibs player would win a league cup winners medal before he had even kicked ball for the club?

15 Who was the Hibs goalkeeper against Rangers in the semi-final of the Skol Cup in 1991?

16 Who was captain of the Ayr United side that defeated Hibs in the semi-final of the competition at Hampden in 2002?

17 Who were Hibs' opponents in the 2007 CIS cup semi-final?

18 During the league cup final victory against Kilmarnock in 2007, only two of the five Hibs substitutes were not used. Goalkeeper Simon Brown was one, who was the other?

19 Who were Hibs' opponents in the league cup semi-final at Tynecastle in 2016, what was the score and who scored the Hibs goals?

20 How many League Cup Finals have Hibs appeared in?

15 HIBS AND HEARTS

1 After leaving the Meadows for a short time in the late 1870s, Hibs and later Hearts would play their home games at which ground?

2 In 1933 a Hibs/Hearts select would play a game to raise money for the dependants of what local tragedy?

3 Who scored a hat trick in the 4-2 victory against Hearts in the game to officially inaugurate the Tynecastle lights in 1957?

4 Who scored Hibs' other goal that evening, his first for the club?

5 The veteran Hearts centre forward Willie Bauld scored his last ever goal against Hibs in a 4-1 victory at Easter Road in January 1962 in a game rearranged from New Year's Day. The future Celtic player Willie Wallace also scored for the visitors, but who was the 17-year-old Heriots schoolboy who would later be a great favourite with the Easter Road fans who scored twice against his future side that afternoon?

6 Instantly recognisable by his sweat soaked jersey, this 'flawed genius' famously scored Hibs' winning goal in the 1965 New Year's Day derby match at Tynecastle from what was said to be a seemingly 'impossible' angle?

7 At the start of the 1965–66 season Hibs defeated Hearts 4-0 at Tynecastle, all the goals scored in the opening 10 minutes. Who were the Hibs goal scorers that afternoon?

8 Who was the last Hibs player to score a hat-trick in a league game against Hearts at Tynecastle?

9 A prolific goal scorer with both Motherwell, Dundee United and later Hearts, which Scottish international player was a provisional

signing at Easter Road in 1970?

10 Name the goal scorers in Hibs' famous 7-0 victory against the Tynecastle side in 1973.

11 Before the 7-0 victory in 1973, what was the highest number of goals scored by Hibs against Hearts in a league game at Tynecastle?

12 Previously with Hearts, which centre-half would win a Scottish Cup winner's medal with Dunfermline against his former side before a move to Coventry, later signing for Hibs from Crystal Palace during the 1974–75 season?

13 Signed from Newcastle United in 1978, which former Hearts player who made almost 100 appearances at Tynecastle and would be a regular at Easter Road for almost eight seasons, played in Scottish Cup Finals for both Edinburgh sides?

14 Which former Hibs and Arsenal player, who at one time was said to be the new George Best, joined Hearts during the 1980-81 season?

15 In season 1999–2000, Hibs defeated Hearts 3-0 at Tynecastle. Dirk Lehmann and Franck Sauzee scored the first two goals. Who scored Hibs' third goal in injury time that afternoon, after coming on as a late substitute?

16 Mixu Paatelainen scored a hat trick in Hibs' 6-2 victory over Hearts at Easter Road in 2000. Who were the other Hibs goal scorers that evening?

17 Before Mixu Paatelainen in 2000, who was the last Hibs player to score a hat-trick against Hearts at Easter Road?

18 In 2002, the Hearts player Mark de Vries scored four goals against Hibs in a league game at Tynecastle. Who was the last

Hearts player before this to score a hat trick against Hibs in a competitive match?

19 What made the 4-4 draw between both Edinburgh sides at Tynecastle on 2 January 2003 particularly painful for the Hibs supporters?

20 On the way to winning the CIS Cup in 2007, Hibs knocked out Hearts at Easter Road. Who scored the only goal of the game?

16 HIBS IN EUROPE

1   In the game against Rot Weiss Essen in 1955, Eddie Turnbull
     became the first ever British player to score a goal in the European
     Cup. Who scored Hibs' second goal that evening in the 4-0
     victory?

2   In 1955, Hibs faced the Swedish side Djurgaardens in the
     European Cup. Why were both the home and away games played
     in Scotland?

3   In the inaugural European Cup competition during the 1955–56
     season, Hibs were defeated at the semi-final stage by the French
     side Stade Reims, who would go on to lose to Real Madrid in
     the final. Who was the player that faced Hibs in both games, and
     would later win the European Cup three times with the Madrid
     side?

4   Why was Hibs' Fairs Cup game against Barcelona at Easter Road
     in December 1960 called off only a few hours before kick-off?

5   When the game against Barcelona did eventually take place, what
     made it another first for the club?

6   Which player famously scored Hibs' winning goal from the
     penalty spot in the Fairs Cup game against Barcelona at Easter
     Road in 1960–61?

7   What tactical ploy did Hibs use against Roma in the away leg of
     the 1960–61 Fairs Cup semi-final in Italy?

8   Hibs lost 6-0 to Roma in the semi-final of the 1960-61 Fairs Cup.
     What was said to have been the main reason behind the heavy defeat?

9   What record did Jimmy O'Rourke establish when making his
     Hibs debut against Utrecht in 1962?

10 Who was the first Hibs player to score a hat trick in a competitive European competition?

11 In the Fairs Cup game against Hamburg at Easter Road in 1969, how did this new ruling confuse the referee at the end of the game?

12 What made Kenny Davidson's European debut for Hibs against Malmo in Sweden in 1970 fairly unusual?

13 In December 1970, Hibs manager Willie MacFarlane was sacked in controversial circumstances just hours before the Easter Road side were to face Liverpool in the Fairs Cup. What was the reason?

14 What colour of jerseys did Hibs wear in the away leg of the Cup Winners Cup against Sporting Lisbon in 1972?

15 Who missed from the penalty spot when Hibs lost a Fairs Cup tie 5-4 on penalties to Leeds United in the Fairs Cup in November 1973 after a 0-0 draw and extra-time, and who were the other Hibs players who scored from the spot that evening?

16 What is Hibs' record victory in a competitive European game?

17 Which aging player came on as a second-half substitute for Juventus in the UEFA Cup game against Hibs in 1974 to completely turn the game in his side's favour?

18 When Hibs played FC Liege in the UEFA Cup at Easter Road in October 1989, the Belgian side featured which player who would soon become world famous for off-field reasons?

19 Why was Hibs' UEFA Cup game in Athens in 2001 initially cancelled?

20 Who scored Hibs goal in the 5-1 defeat in Dnipro, and who was the Hibs manager at the time?

17 JOE BAKER

1   As a youngster, both Joe Baker and his brother Gerry would be
    invited down to London by which English First Division side?

2   When did Joe Baker first come to the attention of Hibs?

3   Which player would be a team mate of Baker's at Armadale, Hibs
    and later Arsenal?

4   Baker had made just one appearance for the reserves before
    making his first team debut, a 8-1 drubbing of East Fife's second
    team. How many goals did the youngster score that afternoon in
    Methil?

5   Who were the opponents when Baker made his first team debut in
    1957?

6   During the clubs summer tour of Spain in 1959, which side were
    reputed to have offered Hibs the equivalent of around £40,000
    for Baker?

7   What made him the star of the show at Tynecastle in March
    1958?

8   Baker scored a hat-trick in Hibs' 6-6 draw with Middlesbrough
    in a friendly match at Easter Road in 1959. Who was the
    Middlesbrough centre forward who scored two goals that evening
    and was vying with the Hibs player for the England centre-
    forward position?

9   Baker won his first full cap against Ireland in 1959. Name the
    famous English international who first recommended the Hibs
    player to the England manager.

10 How did Baker almost miss the start of Hibs' game against

Barcelona at Easter Road in 1961?

11 He famously scored 9 goals against this side in 1961, but was still disappointed. Why?

12 Who were the opponents in Joe Bakers last game for Hibs during his first spell at Easter Road?

13 He scored 159 goals in both spells with the club, 100 before he was 21. He also holds the record for the most number of league goals scored by a Hibs player in a single season. How many?

14 What was his first game back at Easter Road after his move to Italy?

15 What helped bring Bakers time in Italy to an end?

16 After an unhappy spell in Italy with Torino, name the manager who signed Baker for Arsenal in 1962.

17 His international career would suffer what huge disappointment in 1966?

18 On his Easter Road debut, second time around in 1971, Baker caused quite a stir when taking the field against Aberdeen wearing what apparel which was fairly unusual for the time?

19 From which English club was Baker signed from in 1971?

20 What disappointing news did Baker receive on the eve of the Scottish Cup Final in 1972?

18 THE SWINGING '60S

1   Before the start of the 1960–61 season, Hibs transferred two
    players only to soon replace them with two players with the same
    surname. Name the players in question.

2   Eric Stevenson made his Hibs debut against St Johnstone in
    October 1960. Two other players also made their debut for Hibs
    that day. One a former Scottish international, the other a future
    Scottish goalkeeper. Who were they?

3   In the early 1960s, Hibs signed two young players from Hearts
    who would go on to give the club many years of service. Eric
    Stevenson was one in 1960. Who was the other in 1962?

4   In 1962, Hibs tried to sign this unsettled 19-year-old Stirling-born
    player from Leeds United?

5   Which natural phenomenon caused havoc to the game during the
    1962–63 season?

6   When defender Tommy Leishman was signed from Liverpool in
    1963, he would be renewing his acquaintance with Gerry Baker.
    What was the connection between the pair?

7   Who was the Hibs manager who signed Pat Stanton in 1963?

8   During the 1960s, there were three Hibs players who all played
    for the first team and a trainer, all with the same surname,
    although not all at the same time. Who were they?

9   Which long serving defender joined Hibs on the very same day
    that left back John Parke was transferred to Sunderland?

10 In 1964, Hibs won their first silverware since 1952. What was the
    name of the competition and who was the manager at the time?

11 During the 1964–65 season, Hibs achieved which unique feat against Rangers?

12 What major change was made to the ground during the 1965–66 season?

13 He became Hibs first ever official substitute in a game against Clyde during the 1966–67 season. What was his name and who did he replace?

14 Although not used, that same season, which player was the first Hibs player to be listed as a substitute in a domestic game?

15 Which Hibs goalkeeper, who also later played for Hearts and Dundee, won two caps for Scotland in 1974?

16 Which English club did Jim Scott join in 1967?

17 When Colin Stein joined Rangers for a record £100,000 in 1968, which future famous manager was suggested as part-exchange in the deal but turned down the chance of a move to Easter Road?

18 Which Hibs goalkeeper was known as the 'Man in Black'?

19 Signed from Partick Thistle in 1968, who would go on to make a record number of appearances for the club?

20 Making his debut against Dunfermline in 1970, just over a year later, which 19-year-old would make the first of his seven appearances for the full Scotland side in Russia?

19 PAT STANTON

1   On joining Hibs, Pat Stanton was farmed out to which junior club?

2   Stanton made a scoring debut for Hibs' first team against which side?

3   Who were Scotland's opponents when Stanton made his full international debut, and what other Hibs player was also making his debut that evening?

4   Who was the Scotland manager who gave Stanton his debut for the full international side?

5   Who did Pat Stanton replace as captain of Hibs in 1969?

6   Stanton scored one of the Hibs goals in the famous 5-0 victory against the Italian side Napoli in 1967 with a magnificent trademark header. Who were Hibs other goal scorers that evening?

7   What prestigious honour did Pat Stanton receive in 1970?

8   Scoring Hibs first goal in the 2-1 league cup victory against Celtic in 1972, he also scored in the first game of the clubs run to the final that year. Who were the opponents on that occasion?

9   Why was a goal he scored in a league game against Hearts at Tynecastle in November 1975 thought by many, particularly the Hearts supporters, to be controversial?

10 Who did Stanton once say was his second favourite team?

11 What was his nickname at Hibs?

12 In 1975, Stanton joined Celtic in an exchange deal with which player?

13 Who were the opponents in Stanton's last game for Hibs?

14 During his time at Parkhead, Pat would again be selected to represent Scotland. What was the occasion?

15 After leaving Easter Road in 1976, Stanton made 43 competitive appearances for Celtic that season. How many games did he play for the Parkhead side the following season?

16 After his playing days were over, he became assistant to Alex Ferguson at Aberdeen until leaving to manage which Scottish club?

17 Appointed manager of Hibs in 1982, Stanton briefly resigned after a dispute with the board before being persuaded to return. By this time his previous assistants Jimmy O'Rourke and George Stewart had left. Name the former team-mate who was now his assistant manager at Easter Road.

18 Who became Pat Stanton's first big money signing for Hibs?

19 What club provided the opposition for Stanton's testimonial game?

20 How many full caps did Stanton win for Scotland and how many times did he captain the side?

20 TURNBULL'S TORNADOES

1   Who did Eddie Turnbull replace as manager of Hibs in 1971?

2   Which future Scotland manager was very briefly a schoolboy signing at Easter Road under Turnbull in 1971?

3   Who were the opponents in Turnbull's first game as manager at Easter Road?

4   What was the name of Turnbull's first signing for Hibs, from which club was he signed and how did his first game for the club create a possible problem for the new Hibs boss?

5   Which Hibs player was a member of the Scotland XI that faced a Rangers/Celtic select at Hampden in 1971 to raise funds for the Ibrox Disaster appeal?

6   In 1972, which player with something of a bad boy reputation was signed against the rules?

7   The Drybrough Cup was played under which experimental rules in 1972?

8   Which full-back scored twice in an enthralling League Cup tie at Broomfield in 1972?

9   Alex Cropley opened the scoring after only nine seconds in a game against Ayr United at Easter Road just days after Hibs League Cup victory over Celtic in 1972. What was the final score, and who was the Ayr manager that afternoon?

10 Who replaced leg break victim John Brownlie in the side in 1973, what side was he signed from, and what would be his greatest achievement in the game?

11 This was not exactly top of the pops in 1973?

12 A poor game against Hajduk Split in 1973 would hasten the end for which player at Easter Road?

13 After just two league cup appearances during the 1973–74 season, which goalkeeper would play in both legs of the UEFA Cup games against Keflavik?

14 In the opening Drybrough Cup game of the 1973–74 season at Easter Road, these two players would be making their debuts in opposition to each other against their former sides?

15 Hibs defeated Celtic 1-0 in extra-time in the 1973 Drybrough Cup Final at Hampden. Who scored the winning goal?

16 Hibs famously defeated Hearts 7-0 at Tynecastle on the first day of 1973. What was the result when the sides next met at the same ground?

17 Why did Tom Hart ban the TV cameras from Easter Road in 1974?

18 Hibs were leading 2-0 against Celtic at Parkhead in 1975 when, with just minutes remaining the game was abandoned. What was the reason?

19 Which Hibs player would win the League Cup in both Scotland and England during the 1970s?

20 Who scored all five Hibs goals in a friendly against Nijmegen in 1975?

21 THE MANAGERS

1   What was unusual about both managers in the 1923 Scottish Cup
    Final between Hibs and Celtic?

2   Why was the Hibs manager Alec Maley so unpopular with many
    of the Hibs supporters?

3   Which long serving member of the celebrated Hibs side of the
    1920s later became caretaker manager of the club in 1936?

4   Who was the England manager that gave Joe Baker his first
    England cap?

5   Who replaced Hugh Shaw as manager of Hibs in 1961?

6   This player was Jock Stein's first signing for Hibs?

7   Who was the Hibs manager when Hibs defeated Hearts 4-0 at
    Tynecastle, all the goals scored in the first ten minutes of the
    game?

8   Willie MacFarlane managed which club before joining Hibs?

9   Who famously claimed that Rangers were 'rubbish' after a
    Scottish Cup semi-final at Hampden?

10 Why was Eddie Turnbull unhappy with the Leeds manager Don
    Revie after a game at Easter Road in 1974?

11 Who was famously quoted as telling this player that all his brains
    were in his head?

12 Name both the manager and his assistant when Hibs won the
    Second Division title in 1981?

13 Which famous former Scotland captain very briefly replaced Jim Duffy as caretaker manager of the club in 1998 until the arrival of Alex McLeish a few weeks later?

14 Who was the manager of Hibs before Bobby Williamson?

15 How many former Hibs players have managed Scotland?

16 Which Hibs manager once scored a hat-trick for the club against Hearts?

17 A former Hearts player, he was very briefly caretaker manager of the club after Colin Calderwood?

18 What club did Pat Fenlon manage before joining Hibs?

19 What was unusual about Fenlon's first game in charge of Hibs?

20 How many of the Hibs managers since the Second World War have also played for the club?

22 THE 1980S

1   In 1980, which former Clyde player was part of the deal that took Des Bremner to Villa Park?

2   Why did a game in the 1979–80 season manage to attract a crowd more than three times the size of what could normally be expected for a home fixture against the same side?

3   What was Eddie Turnbull's last ever game as manager of Hibs?

4   Which youngster was Turnbull's last signing for the club?

5   With the club now in the first division, which full-back who would go on to be awarded a testimonial at Easter Road was signed from Celtic in January 1981, making his debut in a 2-0 defeat at Starks Park?

6   Who were Hibs' opponents in the last home game of the 1980-81 season that would decide the First Division title, and who scored the home side's goals?

7   Why did this highly rated youngster from Bermuda who played a few reserve games during the 1981–82 season not remain long in Edinburgh?

8   In 1981, this Hibs player made what was surely the shortest league debut in football history?

9   Which international full-back returned to the club from Dundee in season 1981–82?

10 Name the five Hibs players on the books at Easter Road in 1983 that would later go on to have a testimonial at the club?

11 Chairman Tom Hart famously accused this Rangers player of

diving during a game at Easter Road to win a penalty, and would later be fined by the authorities for his remarks?

12 Hibs equalled the Premier League goal scoring record with a home win against which side in 1983?

13 Which former Middlesbrough player would serve a lengthy ban after assaulting a linesman during a game at Easter Road?

14 During a game against Rangers at Ibrox, which young Hibs defender would be attacked by a fan as he stood waiting for a corner kick to be taken?

15 A future Scottish international, which player cost the club in the region of £70,000 when he was signed from East Fife in October 1984?

16 Later a manager of Hibs, who came on as a substitute in the 3-0 League Cup Final defeat by Aberdeen at Hampden in 1985?

17 In the now well-known incident at Easter Road when Graham Souness was sent off on his debut for Rangers in 1986, which player was the only one from both sides to escape either being booked or sent off in the ensuing mayhem?

18 Name the five players signed almost in one fell swoop by John Blackley at the start of the 1986–87 season.

19 The former Rangers player Dougie Bell scored in his first start for the club in a 3-1 victory at Brockville in January 1987. Name the other two players who also made their debut for Hibs that same afternoon.

20 An FA Cup winner, who scored against Hearts at Tynecastle on his debut for Hibs in March 1989?

23 FIRSTS

1 What first did Hibs achieve by winning the Scottish Cup in 1887?

2 Who were the opponents in the first game at the newly re-developed Easter Road in 1924?

3 Who was the first Hibs player to be capped for the full Ireland side?

4 Who was the first Hibs player to be capped for Eire?

5 In 1937, this would break the Easter Road silence?

6 In December 1946, Willie Ormond became an instant favourite with the Easter Road crowd when he scored his first goal for the club against which side?

7 Who made his debut in the 1950 League Cup Final but would never play for the first team again?

8 Against which side did Lawrie Reilly score his first ever hat trick for the club?

9 In 1951, Hibs took part in what was said to have been the first modern floodlit game in Scotland. Who were their opponents and where was the game played?

10 Who scored the very first European Cup goal on British soil?

11 When Joe Baker was first capped by the full England side against Ireland in 1959, his selection completed this international quintet for the club?

12 In an Easter Road career spanning 18 seasons, which legendary player would make his first and only official appearance for the

reserve side near the end of his career?

13 As well as winning the championship with Hibs, Gordon Smith would also achieve the feat with which two other clubs?

14 Frank Haffey of Celtic was in goal when England famously defeated Scotland 9-3 at Wembley in 1961. He wasn't the first choice for the game. Who was?

15 Managing only one first team appearance against St Johnstone in 1965, who would later become the first man to win both of the most famous professional sprint races in the world: the Powderhall Sprint and the Australian Stawell Gift?

16 What was fairly unusual about Hibs' flight to play Sporting Lisbon in the Cup Winners' Cup in 1972?

17 Who scored Hibs first ever Premier League goal in 1975 and who were the opponents ?

18 What change did Hibs make to their jerseys at the start of the 1977–78 season?

19 Who was said to have been the first female director of a Scottish football club when she was appointed in 1987?

20 In 1995 Hibs created history when they became the first Scottish football team to transmit which live domestic football game back to Edinburgh?

24 THE DEVELOPMENT OF EASTER ROAD

1   The record attendance for a game of football in Edinburgh that remains to this day was for a game against Hearts on 2 January 1950. What major development at the stadium at the time made the record attendance possible?

2   In what way in the early 1950s was it made easier for visiting fans, particularly those from outside Edinburgh, to attend games at Easter Road?

3   When the Easter Road floodlights were erected in 1954, the official permission by the Dean of Guilds contained this rather quaint provision?

4   What name was given to the Easter Road floodlighting system by its manufacturers?

5   Who were Hibs' opponents for the inaugural Floodlit game at Easter Road in 1954?

6   In 1955 the removal of which retaining wall at the ground caused a controversy that, for some, still continues to this day?

7   In what year was a new half-time scoreboard erected at the south east corner of the ground?

8   What change would be made to the pitch markings at Easter Road in August 1958?

9   Harry Swan made what suggestion to the city fathers regarding the use of Easter Road stadium for the 1970 Commonwealth games?

10 In what year was the 'Cowshed' at the north end of the ground officially opened?

11 In January 1969 the then Hibs PR man Tommy Younger also took up what position at the club?

12 In what year was under soil heating first installed at Easter Road?

13 Tom Hart made what major purchase in the summer of 1981?

14 Introduced at the stadium as a security measure in 1974, what would be removed in the interests of safety in the wake of the Hillsborough disaster in 1989?

15 In what year was the huge east terracing reduced in size?

16 Which modern piece of electronics appeared at the ground in 1985?

17 Why would waterproof cagoules be required at Easter Road in the mid-1990s?

18 In what year were the present north and south stands constructed?

19 Circumstances in the 1990s almost forced the club to move from Easter Road. Where did it initially propose moving to?

20 What change was made to the pitch in 2000 to comply with UEFA regulations?

25 INTO THE '90S

1   As well as a member of the playing staff, in 1990 who also became assistant to manager Alex Miller?

2   In 1990, which football official was warned by the police not to attend a game at Easter Road?

3   Why was the Hibs side of the early 1990s sometimes referred to as the 'team that would not die'?

4   This future Manchester United manager played against Hibs in the 1991 Skol Cup Final?

5   What personal record did Keith Wright achieve when scoring in the 1991 Final?

6   A former Newcastle United player, who joined Hibs from Dundee United in 1992 and would win Scotland caps while with the Easter Road side?

7   Which future Irish international manager joined the club in 1993?

8   Which player became Hibs' record signing when he returned to the club in November 1994?

9   A goal at Tynecastle in 1994 by this long serving defender ended a dismal run of results for the club in derby games?

10   Which former Hibs player and future manager at Easter Road, he played for Celtic against Hibs in the 1995 Scottish Cup semi-final at Ibrox?

11   Andy Dow scored Hibs' goal in a 1-1 draw at Tynecastle on his debut for the club. What team was he signed from?

12 Who replaced Alex Miller as Hibs' manager in 1996?

13 Which Edinburgh-born centre half would be transferred to the Greek side Ionikos in 1996?

14 This defender with a Bob Marley haircut joined the club from French club RC Lens in 1997.

15 A much travelled footballer, in 1997 he scored the winning goal against Celtic at Easter Road on his Hibs debut after collecting a misplaced pass from Henrik Larsson. Who was it?

16 Who replaced Jim Leighton as the Hibs goalkeeper in 1997?

17 This manager's two sons both played for the club in the 1990s.

18 Then with Liverpool, the former Hibs goalkeeper Tommy Younger captained Scotland in the World Cup Finals in Sweden in 1958, but which goalkeeper actually captained Scotland several times while still a Hibs player?

19 Which French player really got his teeth into the game against Hearts at Easter Road in season 1999–2000?

20 How many competitive European ties did Hibs play between 1990 and 2000?

26 ARE ALL GOALKEEPERS CRAZY?

1   Which Scottish international goalkeeper from the early days of last century was instantly recognisable by the gumboil-like disfigurement on his face?

2   The money received from which goalkeeper's transfer to Arsenal in 1925 is said to have paid for the construction of the new stand at Easter Road?

3   He would be replaced at Easter Road by which goalkeeper who had earlier temporarily taken over from him in the Scotland side because of injury?

4   Thought by many at the time to be the best uncapped goalkeeper in Scotland, which player was signed from junior side Ormiston Primrose before the Second World War and later became a director of the club?

5   A Scottish international and future Hibs goalkeeper, he played for Clyde against Hibs in the Scottish Cup semi-final in 1938. He was also father of two well-known Scottish Rugby internationals. Who was it?

6   A mistake by which young goalkeeper, a future Scottish international, playing one of his very first games for the club, allowed Willie Thornton of Rangers to score the only goal of the game in the Scottish Cup semi-final at Hampden in 1948?

7   In the 1950s, Hibs paid for which international goalkeeper to be flown back from Germany on more than 70 occasions for games?

8   Who played only one first team game for Hibs in 1955 but made European history?

9   Who was the Hibs goalkeeper when Motherwell's Ian St John scored a hat trick in two and a half minutes at Easter Road in 1959?

10 Joe Baker made history when he became the first player from outside the Football League to be capped for the full England side, but he had earlier played for the England under-23's alongside which Hearts player?

11 Signed from Newcastle United in 1960, which veteran goalkeeper would later become the oldest player to make his debut for Scotland although he would not be with Hibs at the time?

12 Goalkeeper Jim Herriot had what strange habit before floodlit games?

13 Who replaced Herriot as goalkeeper at Easter Road and from which club was he signed?

14 In the first game at Tynecastle after Hibs 7-0 victory on New Year's Day the visitors were beaten 4-1. Who was in goal for Hibs that afternoon?

15 Then with Hibs, goalkeeper Alan Rough replaced Jim Leighton at half time in Scotland's 1-1 draw with Wales in September 1985 in unusual circumstances. What was the reason for Leighton's substitution?

16 Who scored a goal against Morton in a league game at Easter Road in 1988?

17 This eccentric Hibs goalkeeper would win the League Cup in both Scotland and England?

18 When Hibs played Rangers in the semi-final of the Skol Cup at Hampden in 1991, who was in goals for Rangers?

19 Which former Aberdeen player and Scottish international was signed from Norwich during the 1997–98 season?

20 Who was the Hibs goalkeeper in the 2007 League Cup Final against Kilmarnock?

27 ODD FACTS

1 The grandfather of which famous Hibs player of the 1880s was a London policeman who first came to Edinburgh to assist in the famous Burke and Hare bodysnatching case?

2 Why would the referee and both teams be fined after a game between Hibs and Hearts at Easter Road in 1912?

3 This Hibs player would be one of the very few fathers and sons to have won the FA Cup?

4 Hibs Summer Cup game against Celtic in 1941 was watched by Easter Road signing target Matt Busby and a friend. This friend, a legendary English outside-right, while also keen to play for the Easter Road side, was unfortunately stationed too far away to make it practical. Who was he?

5 What was significant about Hibs' Scottish Cup semi-final against Rangers at Hampden on 27 March 1948?

6 Hibs are said to have received a bid for Gordon Smith and Bobby Johnstone from this unusual source in the summer of 1953?

7 Tommy Preston scored Hibs' goal in a 1-1 draw with Rangers at Ibrox in September 1954. What was significant about Preston's opponent that afternoon?

8 A Hibs player took part in each of the three high scoring defeats by England at Wembley in 1955, 1961 and 1975. Name the three players involved.

9 What was the result of Hibs game against the Swiss side, Lausanne, in the first round of the Fairs Cup in 1960?

10 Name the two players who would later join Hibs, who became at the time the youngest in Scottish football to make their league

debuts, one in 1945 and the other in 1962?

11 What were the unusual circumstances behind Eric Stevenson signing for Hibs in 1960?

12 Questions were raised in Parliament regarding the signing of which two players in 1978?

13 What was fairly unusual about Hibs' home game against Rangers in December 1971?

14 In Scotland, substitutes were not allowed in domestic games until the start of the 1966–67 campaign, but the previous season which Hibs player had been listed as a substitute in a competitive European game?

15 Since the Second World War, there have been six fathers and sons who have played for the club. Can you name them?

16 In the 1980s, which Hibs goalkeeper shared the same first and last names as a prominent Burnley, Derby County and Wales player, only in reverse order?

17 In what year did Easter Road stadium first become all-seated?

18 Name the five Hibs players that have won the European Cup?

19 What rare occurrence took place during Alan Stubbs first game at the club?

20 What was fairly odd about both goalkeepers in the 2017 Scottish Cup semi-final between Hibs and Aberdeen?

28 HANDS OFF HIBS

1   Who did Duff and Gray purchase the club from in 1987?

2   Name the 'mystery' financial backer that made the purchase possible.

3   These two big money signings were made in 1987 which suggested that the club was in a healthy position financially. What were they?

4   In what year did Hibs become the first Scottish football team to be floated on the Stock (Unlisted Securities) Market?

5   Which well-known Edinburgh comedian was the face of the TV advert to persuade the fans to buy shares?

6   After the Hearts Chairman Wallace Mercer's shock attempt to take over the club in June 1990, which person was elected chairman of the fan-led Hands off Hibs protest committee?

7   Who was the Hibs manager at the time of Mercer's attempted take-over?

8   Which children's TV presenter was seen on the big screen wearing a Hands off Hibs T-shirt?

9   What was the name of the nightclub in the West of England that Hibs purchased for almost one million pounds?

10 Name the chain of pubs and hotels in the West Country that were bought a few months later.

11 After being summoned to a meeting in London to discuss a prospective buyer for the club, who did Duff and Gray initially think the potential buyer might be?

12 Why was a mass protest march through the city refused by the police?

13 At the Hands off Hibs rally at Easter Road, which former Hibs player knelt and kissed the turf to the acclaim of the watching fans?

14 What suggestion did the Edinburgh Council make that would have allowed the club to continue playing if Mercer's attempts had been successful?

15 This well-known Hearts player disobeyed his chairman to speak at the Hands off Hibs Rally at the Usher Hall?

16 During the dispute, a group of Hibs fans made a special visit to Tynecastle. What was the purpose of the visit?

17 Two Hibs fans living in London also made what emotional trip to 10 Downing Street?

18 Mercer's takeover bid would eventually be defeated when he failed to achieve the number of shares required. However after being unable to pay a VAT bill, the receivers would soon be called in to Easter Road. Two Edinburgh businessmen stepped in with plans to save the club. Tom Farmer's bid was one. Who was the other?

19 Who became the Hibs chairman after Tom Farmer's successful bid to save the club?

20 Probably to alleviate the financial position, which Hibs player would be sold to Celtic around the same time?

29 MISCELLANEOUS

1 What was significant about Hibs 9-1 defeat by Dumbarton in Edinburgh on 27 September 1890?

2 Harry Swan held which unofficial position at the club before he became a director in 1931?

3 What was fairly unusual regarding the right back position for Scotland's games against France and Wales in 1948?

4 What was the first ever game involving Hibs to be televised live?

5 Over the years, Hibs had travelled extensively to Europe and Scandinavia. In 1953 they would travel much further afield. What was the destination that year?

6 What was the first ever game at Easter Road to be televised live?

7 Although not directly related to Hibs, the first ever official penalty kick in the world took place just a couple of hundred yards from the present Easter Road Stadium. Where was the game played and who were the teams?

8 Who has scored the most hat-tricks for the club, Gordon Smith, Lawrie Reilly or Joe Baker?

9 This former member of the famous Ancell Babes of the 1950s and early '60s was signed from Blackpool in 1963?

10 Who captained the club in the famous 2-0 victory over Real Madrid at Easter Road in 1964 and what was the name of the 18-year-old that scored Hibs first goal that evening?

11 Why was Willie Hamilton awarded the man-of-the-match trophy after a game against Ottawa in 1965?

12 In the 1960s, which player made an astonishing 273 consecutive appearances for the club?

13 The legendary Bill Shankly would name this former Hibs player in his best ever Liverpool XI?

14 What was unusual about the Hibs line up before the Drybrough Cup game against St Mirren at the start of the 1973–74 season?

15 Who were the opponents in George Best's last official game for the club and what number was he wearing?

16 At the start of the 1979–80 season, this four team Skol Festival tournament took place in Edinburgh involving both Hibs and Hearts, the games played at Easter Road and Tynecastle. Name the managers of both Edinburgh sides and also the two English sides involved.

17 Which former Hearts and Celtic full-back joined Hibs in the summer of 1968?

18 How many different numbered shirts did Joe Baker wear during his two spells with the club?

19 Adopted in England in 1981, which rule change would not come into operation in Scotland until the 1994–95 season?

20 Arthur Duncan has made the most league appearances for Hibs with 446. Who is second?

30 ALMOST THE STORY SO FAR

1 In 2005, Hibs made a poignant return visit to Germany for a friendly game. What was the occasion?

2 The son of which European Cup winner was signed from Livingston in 2006?

3 Who were Hibs opponents when fans favourite Abdessalam Benjelloun made his debut for the club in April 2006?

4 Against which side did Lewis Stevenson make his first team debut?

5 Who was temporarily in charge of team affairs for just over two weeks after the departure of Tony Mowbray to West Bromwich Albion and the introduction of John Collins in October 2006?

6 Which Hibs assistant manager had something in common with full-back David Murphy?

7 Name the Hibs goal scorers in the 2007 CIS Cup final victory against Kilmarnock.

8 In August 2007, he scored the winning goal at Tynecastle after only two minutes on his debut for the club. What was his name and from which club was he signed?

9 In 2008, who scored Hibs' opening goal in a 2-0 home win against Celtic from just inside his opponents half with what he later claimed to be a speciality strike?

10 The former Arsenal player Anthony Stokes would win the Scottish Cup during his second spell at Easter Road, but was earlier on loan with which Scottish club?

11 It was hardly defences on top in this game at Fir Park in the final game of the 2009–10 season. What was the final score and who were the Hibs goal scorers that evening?

12 With which club did Alan Stubbs start his professional playing career and what was his last?

13 David Gray famously scored the winning goal in the 2016 Scottish Cup final against Rangers, who scored Hibs' first goal in that season's run to the final?

14 Two of the Hibs players who took part in the 2016 cup final have won both the Scottish and League Cups. Who are they?

15 From which club did Hibs sign David Gray?

16 An easy one – this magnificent triumph on 21 May 2016 ended 114 years of disappointment?

17 Lewis Stevenson became the only Hibs player to have won both the League Cup and Scottish Cup with the club, but which Hibs player at Hampden that famous afternoon in 2016 already held an FA Cup winner's medal?

18 The former Hibs player and Norwegian international, Nikolas Gunnarsson, was also eligible to play for which country?

19 How many goals did Jason Cummings score on Hibs' march to the 2016 Scottish Cup Final?

20 Scottish Cup hero goalkeeper Conrad Logan joined Hibs on a short term deal from Rochdale near the end of the 2015–16 season where he had been on loan, but he was still a registered player with which English side?

31 DEFINITELY THE LAST WORD

1 How many of the Scottish Cup winning squad were no longer at Easter Road at the start of the 2017–18 season?

2 Who scored Hibs' first league goal of the 2017–18 season?

3 From which club did Hibs sign Marvin Bartley?

4 How many league games did Danny Swanston play for Hearts?

5 Easter Road housed Hibs' biggest home crowd of the season against which side in December 2017?

6 After loan spells at Rotherham and Dutch side Breda, which left sided England youth international scored his first goal for the club in a 2-1 victory over Motherwell in January?

7 In how many league games did Hibs fail to score in season 2017–18?

8 John McGinn is now a regular member of the Scotland Squad. Against which side did he make his full international debut?

9 How many hat-tricks were scored by Hibs in league games during the season?

10 How many Hibs goalkeepers were listed, either as first choice or as a substitute for the first team during season 2017–18?

11 With which club did forward Oli Shaw play before joining Hibs?

12 How many appearances did Faycal Rherras make for the first team during the season?

13 What was the highest number of goals scored by Hibs in a single

game during the 2017–18 season?

14 A Leicester City player Neil Lennon was involved in a well-publicised altercation with which English international?

15 During the 2017–18 season, Hibs had three players that had signed for the club at least twice. Who were they?

16 Who were the opponents in Neil Lennon's first game as manager of Hibs?

17 For what country did goalkeeper Ofir Marciano gain full international caps?

18 What side ended Hibs 2017–18 League Cup aspirations?

19 Which Hibs player made the most first team appearances in all games during the season?

20 Why were the Hibs supporters Celtic fans for the day on 19th May 2018?

THE HISTORY OF THE HIBS
QUIZ BOOK

ANSWERS

I IN THE BEGINNING

1 Hibernian Football Club was formed by a group of Irishmen and descendants of Irishmen living in Edinburgh who decided to adopt the Roman or Latin name for Ireland, Hibernia. The colours are the traditional Irish green.

2 The club's first recorded game took place on Christmas Day 1875 at the East Meadows, a large expanse of open public land in the south of the city against a side that were destined to become their greatest rivals, Heart of Midlothian. Seemingly, despite playing for around 20 minutes with only eight men, their opponents still managed to record a slender 1-0 victory.

3 The Catholic Young Men's Society. The Edinburgh branch of the CYMS had been formed in 1865 overseen by Father Hannan from St Patrick's Church in the Cowgate. Under the influence of the church the football club would later benefit from the use of the institute in St Mary's Street as a meetings place, and also with changing facilities on match days at church premises in Lothian Street, only a short distance from the Meadows.

4 Originally refused permission to join the recently formed Edinburgh Football Association and informed that they would have to join the Scottish Football Association first, they were also rejected by the SFA who claimed that they catered for Scotsmen and not Irishmen. Reason would soon prevail however, and with the backing of several prominent football players in the area the club was eventually allowed to join both organisations.

5 Although the first club rules state that the club colours should be white Guernsey's and white trousers with green stripes it is now generally believed that the first jerseys were dark green and white hoops with the letters HFC in large black Gothic letters emblazoned across the chest. A photograph from 1876 shows the players wearing the hooped jerseys and it seems highly unlikely that the club would

have changed attire after just a few games.

6   Before a move to the Catholic Institute in St Mary's Street, Hibs'
    early meetings had been held in Buchanan's Temperance Hotel in the
    High Street which was also a popular meeting place for several other
    sides around that time.

7   With the Meadows now becoming overpopulated by several of the
    new teams that were springing up in the city around this time, some
    of the more ambitious sides would be forced to look elsewhere for
    their own home grounds.

8   Hibs first captain Michael Whelahan, who had been born at Kilglass
    in Ireland, was the great, great uncle of the legendary Pat Stanton
    who by coincidence was the Hibs captain during the clubs centenary
    year in 1975.

9   There were actually two. Both James McGhee and James Lundie
    were part of the Scotland side that defeated Wales 4-1 at First
    Hampden on 10 April 1886. It would be their first and only
    appearance for their country.

10 Although in the early days the club would play at various venues
    throughout the city it is generally accepted that Hibs have had five
    home grounds: The Meadows, Mayfield, Powderhall, the first Easter
    Road (The Hibs Supporters Club and car park now partly occupy
    the site) and the present Easter Road.

11 Hibs' very first Scottish Cup tie was against neighbours Hearts at the
    East Meadows on 29 September 1877, the game ending 0-0. Hibs
    would win the replay 2-1 at the same venue a week later watched by
    crowd of well over 1,000, an impressive attendance for a game of
    football at that time.

12 On 7 May 1881, Hibs Easter Road ground was the venue for
    the world's first ever women's international match when a side
    representing Scotland faced an England XI, Scotland winning 3-0.

With Scotland turning out in blue jerseys, white knickerbockers and
red stockings and England in blue and white jerseys complete with
white knickerbockers and blue stockings, a player with the poetic
sounding name of Miss Lilly St Clair is credited as having scored the
world's first ever goal in a women's international football match.

13 It was the first time that Hibs had played a game outside of Scotland.
The short tour of England would end in a 4-2 defeat by Rovers, a
4-3 victory against Bolton Wanderers and 2-0 defeat by Blackburn
Olympia.

14 The game took place at Powderhall on a site now occupied by the
Council refuse incinerator. Played during a snowstorm and in front
of only a few hundred hardy souls, the three generators providing
the light would all eventually fail to function properly, the game
ending in near darkness. The experiment was obviously not a success
and it would be many years before the lighting of football matches
would become the accepted norm.

15 In the 1879 final Hibs defeated city rival Hearts 2-0 at Union Park
in Corstorphine after a replay. The first game at Powburn had ended
1-1, a protest by the Hibs players that a late Hearts equaliser should
not have been allowed to stand because of an infringement had led
to the spectators entering the pitch in an attempt to assault some
of the Hearts players, one man requested to appear in court on the
Monday morning.

16 In 1883 Hibs had again reached the final, but because of a mounting
injury list claimed to have been unable to raise a team and requested
a temporary postponement. This arrangement however did not
suit their opponents Edinburgh University and Hibs were forced to
withdraw, giving the university the cup by default.

17 Hibs' record all time victory is 22-1 in a friendly match against the
Black Watch Highlanders, then based at Edinburgh Castle, at the
first Easter Road on 3 September 1881.

18 In 1883, three Lugar Boswell players, Peter McGinn, James McGhee and James McLaren who had earlier impressed in a friendly game, were all signed by the Edinburgh side. They would go on to serve Hibs well for a number of years, McGhee captaining the side to Scottish Cup success in 1887.

19 It is said that the future Hibs manager Willie McCartney's father, John McCartney, who like his son would later manage Hearts, was in the Cowlairs side that faced Hibs in May 1888 in a game to officially open the first Celtic Park.

20 'Darling' Willie Groves had joined the club as a 16-year-old in time for the 1885–86 season, quickly becoming a favourite with the fans. A Scottish Cup winner in 1887 and capped for Scotland against Wales in 1888 in a game played at the first Easter Road ground, Groves was among of a group of players who left to join the newly formed Celtic in 1888. Transferred to the then professional West Bromwich Albion in 1890 where he would win the FA Cup, he would later join Aston Villa, winning the title with the midlands club in 1894 before a brief return to Hibs 1896 to take part in that year's Scottish Cup Final defeat by Hearts. He would die in Edinburgh from TB in 1908 aged only 39.

2   THE EARLY YEARS

1   By this time Hearts had taken over the lease of Powderhall after Hibs' temporary return to Mayfield. A dispute regarding the lease of the ground including a claim that the rent had not been paid resulted in the game being cancelled and the Hearts players and officials ejected from the ground by the police. When the game did eventually take place two weeks later, Hibs defeated their rivals 2-1 at Mayfield.

2   In 1909 James McGhee, one of the players signed from Lugar Boswell six years before became the manager of Hearts, but probably because of his Hibs connections he was not overly popular with the fans and left the following year. He emigrated to America in 1910 where he died in 1941. He was inducted into the Hibernian Hall of Fame in 2010.

3   Hibs first game to officially open their new Easter Road ground was a 5-0 victory in a challenge match against the Edinburgh side Hanover on 14 February 1880.

4   In 1881, the Edinburgh Association Cup was replaced by the Edinburgh Association Shield, later better known as the East of Scotland Shield. Hibs first game for the new silverware was a 4-2 victory against Hearts on 1 October that same year. Now competed annually by youth sides from both Hibs and Hearts it is the third oldest trophy in world football still to be played for today.

5   In 1887, Hibs defeated Vale of Leven in the semi-final of the Scottish Cup only for the West Coast side to protest that the Easter Road player Willie Groves had been paid more than just his expenses, making him a professional which was strictly against the rules at the time. After the original hearing to consider the case had ended undecided, Hibs would eventually win the appeal, but amazingly this would not be heard until a few days after the final itself had been played, and only then on the deciding vote of the chairman.

6   The 1887 Scottish Cup Final took place at Second Hampden before
     Queens Park's move to the present Hampden in 1903. The ground
     would later be renamed Cathkin Park and was home to Third
     Lanark until the clubs demise in 1967.

7   In a ceremony in Glasgow immediately after winning the Scottish
     Cup in 1887, the Hibs secretary James McFadden was heard telling
     a group of local businessmen that they should start their own
     football team. It was a suggestion that would come back to haunt
     him and the club in spectacular fashion when the soon to be formed
     Celtic would poach many of Hibs better players, severely weakening
     the Edinburgh side, and would be one of the contributory factors
     that would eventually lead to the clubs temporary demise in 1891.

8   Injured in the semi-final against Renton in 1887, Gerry Reynolds
     would miss Hibs Scottish Cup victory against Dumbarton in 1887.
     Later after a move to Parkhead he would be part of the Celtic side
     that won the Scottish Cup for the very first time in 1892 when
     defeating Queens Park 5-1 in the final.

9   On 13 August 1887, Hibs defeated Preston North End 2-1 at the
     first Easter Road. Unofficial or not, Hibs would be crowned 'World
     Champions' by the local press. Preston would soon become known
     as 'The Invincibles' after managing to complete the entire 1888–89
     league season undefeated. The following season, this time with the
     agreement of the football authorities on both sides of the border,
     Renton would claim the title of World Champions by defeating West
     Bromwich Albion. It would never be played for again.

10 After service with Celtic, the former Hibs player Willie Groves joined
     Aston Villa from West Bromwich Albion in 1893 and was said to
     have been the first ever player to be transferred for over £100. At
     Villa Park he would help his to the title in 1894.

11 After the exodus of players to the newly formed Celtic in 1888 that
     had severely weakened the side and 18 months after losing the lease
     of the ground at Easter Road, Hibs had been temporarily forced

out of business in 1891. Now playing at the present Easter Road the club had been reformed in time to take its place in the inaugural Second Division Championship in 1893.

12 At that time promotion and relegation was not automatic but only by election and that first year third placed Clyde would be promoted instead of champions Hibs. The Easter Road side would again win the championship the following season, but this time they could not be denied and took their place in the Scottish First Division for the very first time.

13 The start of Hibs game against Celtic at Parkhead in November 1896 was delayed after several of the Celtic players refused to take part in the game until newspaper reporters from the *Glasgow Evening News* and the *Scottish Referee* were removed from the press box after they had heavily criticised the Parkhead side in their game against Rangers the previous week. Manager Maley however flatly refused to accede to the players demands. Three Celtic players, Meechan, Battles and Divers still refused to play and the game went ahead with the home side fielding just ten men until another could be recruited, the game eventually ending 1-1. All three players would later be suspended by the club.

14 The 1896 Scottish Cup Final was played at Logie Green in Edinburgh then the home ground of St Bernard's, Hibs losing 3-1. To this day it is the only Scottish Cup Final ever to have taken place outside of Glasgow. Today Logie Green Road and the surrounding houses occupy the site of the pitch.

15 It was claimed that Hibs winning goal against Celtic in the 1902 Scottish Cup final had been scored after the Hibs player Bobby Atherton had confused a Celtic defender by shouting 'leave it' at a corner allowing McCartney to back-heel the only goal of the game past the Celtic goalkeeper McFarlane. Disputed or not it was the goal that gave Hibs the Scottish Cup for a second time.

16 The Cup final was originally to have taken place at Ibrox, but just

days before 25 fans had been killed and well over 500 injured when part of the wooden terracing had collapsed during Scotland's game against England, and even although it was the home ground of one of the finalists, with the new Hampden Park not yet ready, the game had been switched to Parkhead.

17 Just weeks after the Scottish Cup final success, Hibs defeated the Parkhead side 6-2 in the Glasgow Charity Cup Final at Hampden. It was the third time that the Easter Road side had taken part in the competition, losing in the first round on both the previous occasions in 1887 and 1888. However, the following year Celtic would gain sweet revenge on the Edinburgh side with a 5-0 victory at Cathkin in the semi-final after a 0-0 draw in the first game.

18 Phil Kelso managed Hibs for one season in 1903-04 before taking over at newly promoted Arsenal where he would remain for four seasons. He would later spend 15 years with Fulham, and to this day is still the London clubs longest serving manager.

19 In 1905, the club proposed moving to a brand new purpose built ground at Piershill. The move would never take place. Although a pitch had been laid out Hibs never played a game at the ground, the arena staging mostly minor matches, greyhound racing, athletics and cycling. An attempt by the nomadic Leith Athletic to play their home games there came to nothing and by the end of the 1920s the area lay in a derelict condition and was finally demolished around 1931. Today both the south eastern extension of Piershill Cemetery and the adjacent Mountcastle housing estate occupy the site of the once highly enterprising but ultimately doomed undertaking.

20 On Christmas Day 1909, the Scottish international James Main, captain for the day, was severely injured after an accidental collision with an opponent. Taken from the field, he recovered enough after the game to be able to make his way to his home to West Calder. Later that night his condition worsened and he was rushed to Edinburgh Royal Infirmary where, despite an emergency operation, he died three days later. He is buried in West Calder Cemetery.

3   THE FIRST WORLD WAR

1   Paddy Callaghan joined Hibs from Jordanhill in 1899 and would serve the club loyally for almost 15 seasons. Although still a registered player, he does not appear to have made any appearances for the first team in the 1914–15 season and would soon hang up his boots.

2   Sadly, Welshman Bobby Atherton who had captained the club to victory in the Scottish Cup Final in 1902 as well as its first ever League Championship success in 1903 was drowned in 1917 when his merchant ship the Britannia making its way from Middlesbrough to San-Malo in France with a consignment of Pig Iron was torpedoed in the English Channel by the German Submarine UC75. The exact location of the wreck would not be discovered for several years.

3   During the First World War young men who were not in uniform would often be handed a white feather in the street by women as a sign of cowardice.

4   The Leith-born Harry Swan.

5   Both Hibs and Hearts provided players for a game against an international select at Tynecastle to raise funds for the Belgian Relief Appeal. Both Hibs, Hearts and many others, would play numerous games during the war to raise money for charitable causes.

6   Fortunately the father and two uncles of the future legendary Hibs player Bobby Combe would survive the horrific rail accident at Gretna in May 1915 involving the 7th Royal Scots, a regiment that had been raised in Leith. The death toll of 216 remains to this day the highest number of dead in a rail accident in this country.

7   Both Easter Road and the Hibs ground at Piershill were used by the Royal Scots for the training of new recruits.

8 Jimmy Hendren, who had been signed from Cowdenbeath in 1911, was a great uncle of Pat Stanton on his maternal side. Because he had just become a father his enlistment into the armed forces had been temporarily deferred, but unfortunately he would die in the Edinburgh Royal Infirmary of natural causes a short time later.

9 In 1915 the Scottish Second Division was suspended for the duration of the war. It would not be revived until season 1921–22 but now for the first time with promotion and relegation automatic.

10 During 1915–16 and 1916–17, the league consisted of 20 teams, reduced to 18 for both the 1917–18 and 1918–19 seasons.

11 Sergeant Patrick 'Paddy' Hagan, a popular player with Hibs during the early years of the century was killed at the battle of the Somme in July 1916 while serving with the 11th Battalion Royal Scots. Then aged almost 37, Hagan had also seen service in the Boer War. Like many thousands of others, he has no known grave, and is commemorated on the Thiepval Memorial in France.

12 The Prestonpans born Peter Kerr, who had joined the club in 1909 and would stun the Hibs support when he crossed the city in 1925 to join rivals Hearts, had played in all three finals.

13 Sadly, Dan McMichael, who had kept the club going throughout the turbulent years of conflict, would succumb to the great influenza pandemic that swept Europe during the closing days of the war and died in February 1919.

14 Dan McMichael was replaced as manager of Hibs by Alex Maley. After spells managing Clyde and Clydebank, Maley was manager at Easter Road between 1921–1925 leading the club to successive Scottish Cup finals in 1923 and 1924. After leaving Easter Road he would manage Crystal Palace for a few seasons before returning to Scotland for a second spell with Clydebank.

15 Robert Wilson, who sadly lost his life weeks before the end of the war.

16 As well as playing in the consecutive 1923 and 1924 Scottish Cup Finals, later as Hibs manager Hugh Shaw would lead the club to three League Championships in the immediate post-war years and also into the inaugural European Cup. He remains to this day Hibs most successful manager ever.

17 Leith born Sandy Grosert, a registered Hibs player between 1911–1920, would win the Military Cross in 1918 for conspicuous gallantry at the battles for Rouex and Greenland Hill. Although badly gassed and wounded he would return to Easter Road after the war before ending his playing career with Dunfermline in 1924 after a short spell with Aberdeen. The former Hibs player John Sharp would also win the Military Cross during the conflict, and George Rae who had played for the club until enlisting in the armed forces at the outbreak of hostilities would be awarded The Italian Silver Medal of Honour. Four current and seven former Hibs players would lose their lives during the First World War.

18 After struggling near the foot of the table for some time Hibs would end the 1918–19 season 18th in the table, or rock bottom, and only the fact that there was no Second Division at the time would save the club from the humiliation of relegation.

19 The Scottish Cup was not competed for between 1914 and 1920.

20 Both Edinburgh clubs would join forces in a game to raise funds for the construction of the War Memorial at Haymarket.

4   HIBS AND THE SCOTTISH CUP

1. In 1874 Queens Park defeated Clydesdale 2-0 in the first ever Scottish Cup Final. Queens Park would win the first three competitions, and six of the first nine. Vale of Leven won the trophy on three consecutive years between 1877 and 1879.

2. In the 1914 Scottish Cup final, the last before the First World War, Hibs were beaten 4-1 by Celtic at Hampden after a replay, the first game ending 0-0.

3. In one of his first games for the Parkhead side centre-forward Jimmy McColl would score twice in the eventual 4-1 victory over Hibs in 1914. Later he would be part of the Hibs side of the 1920s that reached consecutive Scottish Cup finals in 1923 and 1924, unfortunately losing both. McColl's medals from these games and numerous others from a glittering career would later be stolen during a burglary at his house.

4. Despite Johnny Cuthbertson giving Hibs the lead in the very first minute of the 1947 final, the Easter Road side would eventually lose 2-1. South African Stan Williams who had made almost two dozen appearances as a guest for the Easter Road side during the war years scored the winning goal from a seemingly almost 'impossible angle' on the by-line just before half-time.

5. By that time Weir had been transferred to Blackburn Rovers in a then record equalling £10,000 deal. He would later return to Scotland to sign for Celtic before eventually ending his career with the Irish side Portadown after spells with Falkirk, Llanelli and Dumbarton.

6. The 1947 Scottish Cup Final was the first time that the cup had been presented to the winning side on the field after the game. Previously it had been presented to the winners in the dressing room. It was also the first time that medals had been awarded to the losers.

7 The Hibs manager Willie McCartney had complained of feeling unwell during the game and was driven back to his home in Edinburgh while the match was still taking place. At home he would suffer a massive heart attack, dying later that evening, his death stunning the football world.

8 Watched by a crowd of well over 100,000 at Ibrox, Rangers had twice taken the lead only for Gordon Smith and Eddie Turnbull to equalise. Late in the game Bobby Johnstone would give Hibs a famous victory by scoring the winner following a free kick taken by Eddie Turnbull. Although somewhat exaggerated, one newspaper the following morning claimed the victory as 'the finest thing the Easter Road side had ever done.'

9 In the replayed cup semi-final against Rangers at Hampden in 1958 Hibs had been leading 2-1 when the Glasgow side appeared to have equalised late in the game. Referee Davidson had initially awarded the goal only to be informed by his linesman that a Rangers player had punched the ball out of the Hibs goalkeeper Lawrie Leslie's hands, a decision later confirmed by TV and newspaper photographs to have been correct. Davidson had been due to referee Rangers next game the following week only for Scottish League to be contacted by the Ibrox who informed them that on the advice of the police who feared trouble, Davidson was not to take charge of the game. On investigation it was found that the police had no knowledge of the incident and Rangers would later be severely censured by the football authorities.

10 An injury to the long serving John Paterson leading up to the game had allowed the young centre-half Jackie Plenderleith, who had only occasionally featured in the first team that season although he had played in a couple of the earlier rounds, to take the experienced Paterson's place in the line up for the cup final.

11 Only two, Eddie Turnbull and Willie Ormond. Lawrie Reilly had recently announced his retirement and had made his last ever appearance against Rangers at Easter Road just few days before the

final. Bobby Johnstone was now at Manchester City and Gordon Smith injured.

12 Despite scoring first Hibs would lose 2-1 at Tynecastle in a game that had previously been postponed because of the weather. The Hibs left back Joe Davis missed a penalty, his first miss from the spot after six previous attempts since taking over as the regular penalty taker.

13 Arthur Duncan was the only Hibs player to feature in both the 1972 and 1979 finals. Duncan had received a head knock during the heavy cup final defeat by Celtic in 1972 and would spend a few days in hospital suffering from concussion. In the second replay of the 1979 final he famously scored the spectacular own goal that would give Rangers an eventual 3-2 victory and the cup.

14 After almost 20 years as a professional, the cup final would turn out to be Bertie Auld's last ever appearance in senior football when he replaced the injured Arthur Duncan in the second half. He would soon accept the position of trainer at Easter Road and would later go on to manage the club.

15 In a game against Falkirk at Brockville in February 1972 the Scottish international Alex Cropley was involved in a tackle with the future Manchester United manager Alex Ferguson that resulted in him breaking an ankle and he would miss the rest of the season. Hibs would eventually win the game 3-2, Johnny Hamilton giving the Easter Road side the lead after just ten seconds. Late in the game Ferguson was sent off after an over robust tackle on left back Erich Schaedler before substitute Joe Baker, making his long awaited comeback from injury, scored the winner in the dying minutes with a diving header.

16 The Scottish Cup. Although the FA Cup tournament is older, the Wanderers winning the first competition in 1871–72, the original trophy won by Aston Villa in 1910 was stolen from a Birmingham shop window. The Scottish Cup, first played for in season 1873–74 and won by Queens Park is the original and the oldest national

football association trophy in the world. Both cups have now been replaced by replicas, the present FA Cup in 1992. The original Scottish Cup is presented to the winning captain on the day which is then taken from him in the dressing room to be replaced by a replica.

17 Signing for the club in 1999 from Montpelier, the 39 times capped French international and European Cup winner with Marseille Franck Sauzee captained the side in the 3-0 defeat by Celtic in the 2001 Scottish Cup Final. He would later manage the club for a short time before returning to France to become a TV pundit.

18 Born in Gambia, left back Pa Kujabi joined Hibs from German side Frankfurt in 2012. He was sent off in the Scottish Cup final against Hearts just a few months later. Booked in the first half he received a second yellow card within minutes of the restart after bringing down a Hearts player that resulted in a penalty for the opponents. TV evidence later seemed to suggest that the original offence had taken place outside the box. Regardless, Kujabi was sent off, leaving his team mates to play the remainder of the game with ten men, resulting in a heavy defeat for the Easter Road side.

19 Hibs have been involved in 14 Scottish Cup Finals since the beginning. 1887, 1896, 1902, 1914, 1923, 1924, 1947, 1958, 1972, 1979, 2001, 2012, 2013, and 2016, winning three, 1887, 1902 and famously in 2016.

20 Because the ribbons featured the name of sponsors William Hill the bookmakers, they were not allowed to be displayed on the cup during visits to the schools.

5 THE ROARING '20S

1   From the 11 Hibs players that took part in the 1914 Scottish Cup
Final against Celtic, only the long serving Peter Kerr and Matthew
Paterson would play regularly for the club during the early years of
the new decade, Bobby Templeton to a lesser degree. Paterson moved
to St Bernard's in 1923 after 15 seasons at Easter Road and in 1926
Kerr would cross the city to sign for Hearts. Templeton, who himself
would spend 16 seasons at Easter Road would go on to manage the
club between 1925 and 1936.

2   In 1921 the league was increased from 18 teams to 22. The Second
Division that had been suspended during the First World War would
be resurrected the following season.

3   The first Hibs player to appear at Wembley in an international
match was goalkeeper Willie Harper, the game ending in a 1-1 draw.
It was Harper's sixth appearance for Scotland.

4   In the 1923 final Celtic defeated Hibs 1-0, Airdrie winning 2-0 the
following year.

5   As part of the celebrated side that contested both the 1923 and 1924
Scottish Cup Finals, the long serving defensive partnership of Willie
McGinnigle and Willie Dornan would go on to serve the club well
throughout most of the 1920s.

6   None. Of the 11 New Year's Day games played between 1920 and
1930 Hibs would win seven, the other four drawn.

7   An inspirational figure in the side in the run up to the final, an
uncharacteristic mistake by goalkeeper Willie Harper, who hesitated
in coming out for a cross ball, allowed Celtic to score the only goal
of the game. It would be the only goal conceded by Hibs in that
year's competition.

5

8   The 1924 Scottish Cup Final between Hibs and Airdrie was played
    at Ibrox.

9   As part of the complete renovation of the Easter Road ground in
    1924 the previous structures on the east side of the ground were
    swept away and a new Main Stand erected on the west side of the
    ground. The pitch was also moved several yards to the east and
    slightly levelled although it still retained its famous slope.

10 With the new Easter Road stand not yet ready, at the beginning
    of the 1924–25 season Hibs played a couple of 'home games' at
    Tynecastle, against Partick Thistle and Motherwell, winning both. At
    that time work was also being carried out at the Gymnasium ground
    and with St Bernard's also sharing Tynecastle, Hibs were required to
    play their games in Gorgie on a Friday evening.

11 Only two players were now required to be between the ball and
    the goal before you could be declared offside instead of the three as
    before.

12 The Rangers goalkeeper Willie Robb would take over from the
    injured Willie Harper as Scotland's goalkeeper in the 3-0 victory
    against Wales in Cardiff in October 1925. On Harpers transfer
    to Arsenal a few months later Robb would sign for the Easter
    Road side and win one more cap in a 2-2 draw with Wales at the
    Racecourse in Wrexham in 1927. The goalkeeper would form the
    last line of the Easter Road defence between 1926 and 1930 before
    leaving to join Aldershot.

13 The popular wing-half Peter Kerr had played in both the 1923 and
    1924 Scottish Cup finals. Although then thought to be approaching
    the end of his playing days Kerr was such a popular figure at Easter
    Road that many Hibs supporters were stunned when he was given
    a free transfer, particularly the fact that he then joined great rivals
    Hearts. He would go on to give Hearts five seasons as first team
    regular before joining Leith Athletic, finally ending his playing career
    with Inverness Caledonian in 1933 aged 42.

14 Inside forward Jimmy Dunn was a member of the immortal Scottish side that defeated the much fancied England 5-1 at Wembley in 1928 to be acclaimed 'The Wembley Wizards' a side still revered to this day in Scottish football folklore.

15 McColl had a short period managing Belfast Celtic, leading the Irish club to the league championship.

16 Outside-right Harry Ritchie would follow inside-right Jimmy Dunn to Goodison a few weeks later. Dunn would later score in Everton's 3-0 victory over Manchester City in the 1933 FA Cup Final.

17 On 19 January 1929 all five Edinburgh clubs would be defeated in the first round of that year's Scottish Cup competition, Hibs losing 2-1 to St Johnstone at Easter Road. Hearts were defeated by Airdrie, Leith Athletic by Motherwell, St Bernard's by Falkirk and Edinburgh City thrashed 11-1 by Rangers at Ibrox.

18 Ayr United's 2-1 victory over Kilmarnock would condemn second bottom Hibs to relegation for the first time in the clubs history.

19 Bobby Templeton would manage the club from 1925 until 1936 before being replaced by former team mate Johnny Halligan who took over as caretaker manager until the appointment of Willie McCartney later that same year. Hugh Shaw would replace McCartney as manager in 1948.

20 Although the club had lost several inspirational players during this time it was generally accepted that the cancellation of the reserve side to save money when the ground was being developed in the mid-20s had led to a lesser calibre of player breaking through and that this had not helped in the fight against relegation at the end of the decade.

5

6 THE INTERNATIONAL GAME

1 Willie Groves was the first Hibs player to score a goal for Scotland in the 5-1 victory against Wales on 10 March 1888, the game played at the first Easter Road. It was the first time that a home international game had taken place outside of Glasgow. It would be Groves only appearance for his country while at Hibs. Later after joining Celtic he would make another two international appearances, scoring a hat-trick against Ireland at Ibrox in 1889.

2 Bobby Atherton was capped by Wales in a 4-0 defeat by England in Bristol in 1899. Atherton would make nine appearances for his country: five while a Hibs player, but would never end on the winning side although three of the games had been drawn.

3 The record holder before Reilly was goalkeeper Harry Rennie who during his time with Hibs would win 11 caps for Scotland between the years 1901–1908. He had also been capped twice while with Hearts.

4 Goalkeeper Jim Leighton, who would win 23 of his 91 full Scotland caps while at Easter Road.

5 Right-back Hugh Howie scored on his international debut in Scotland's 3-1 victory against Wales at Cardiff in 1948. It would be one of only two goals the player would score during a distinguished career. Sadly Howie would soon contract TB, then a far more serious illness than today, and would miss a large part of the following season. However he would return to the side in time to add another two league championship medals to the one from 1948. After hanging up his boots he became a reporter for the Daily Express but it was while working for the Glasgow based newspaper that he was killed in a road accident just outside Glasgow in January 1958 aged just 33.

6 Lawrie Reilly scored three times in Scotland's 6-0 victory against the

United States at Hampden in April 1952, his 17th appearance for the full international side.

7 Eddie Turnbull made nine appearances for the full Scotland side between 1948–1958. Most record books list the number of appearances as only eight, but he was also capped against France in May 1948 which for some reason has been omitted from most official lists.

8 Born in Liverpool during the war the family moved back to Scotland when Joe Baker was only a few weeks old to escape the bombing of the port. At that time you had to play for the country of your birth and in 1959 Baker made football history when becoming the first ever player from outside the Football League to be capped at full level by England, scoring once in a 2-1 victory against Ireland at Wembley in November.

9 Alex Cropley. Although born in Aldershot where his father was turning out for the local league side, a change in the regulations in 1971 now allowed a player to play for a country of his parent's birth making Cropley eligible to play for Scotland.

10 The then Scotland manager Tommy Docherty publicly acclaimed Stanton as being a far better player than the England World Cup winning captain Bobby Moore. Incredibly just a few months later Docherty, questioning the player's loyalty after he had been forced to withdraw from Scotland's trip to Brazil during the summer on doctor's orders, stated that the Hibs player would never be selected for the country again while he was manager, a decision however that he was eventually forced to overturn.

11 Injured during the game against Belgium, Alex Cropley would be replaced by Kenny Dalglish of Celtic who would be making the first of his 102 appearances for Scotland. Although Cropley had been listed as a substitute in a game against Germany in 1974 he was not called upon and would never play for the full Scotland side again.

12 Although born in Liverpool during the war the Baker family had returned to Scotland when Joe was only a few weeks old and were then living in the Motherwell area. At that time schoolboys were allowed to play for the country they resided in and Baker was selected for the Scotland Schoolboys side against England schools at Goodison in 1954. In 1959 he would become the first player from outside the Football League to be capped for the full England side and the first at that time not to have played for an English side, Owen Hargreaves the only other to have achieved that feat to this day. Baker would later play for the full England side against Scotland at Hampden in 1960 to also become the first to represent both countries.

13 Rioch and Cropley were both born in Aldershot and both would later go on to play for Scotland.

6

14 Joe Baker's brother Gerry who would later also play for Hibs, was born in New York making him eligible to play for America and he would go on to represent the USA seven times.

15 Neil Martin was at inside left in Scotland's victory over the red-hot favourites Italy in 1965, John Greig famously scoring the winner in the late stages of the game after a tremendous through pass from team mate Jim Baxter. Unfortunately Scotland would fail to qualify for the Finals in England after a 3-0 defeat in Italy with an injury ridden patched up side.

16 Teenager Peter Cormack made an impressive Scotland debut against a Brazil side that included the great Pele in a 1-1 draw at Hampden during one of Brazil's warm up games for the forthcoming World Cup Finals in England.

17 None. Although Stein had been selected for Scotland's game against Denmark in Copenhagen while he was still a Hibs player, by the time the game took place a few days later he had signed for Rangers for a then Scottish record fee of £100,000. His then former team mate Peter Cormack replaced Jim McCalliog late in a game that ended 1-0

in Scotland's favour.

18 Hibs legendary defender Erich Schaedler had been born in Scotland, the son of a German soldier captured during the Second World War. He would win his only Scotland cap in a game against Germany in Frankfurt in March 1974, and although he had been included in the pool for the World Cup Finals in Germany a few months later he would not be called upon.

19 Joe Harper would play four times for the full Scotland side, three of his appearances against Denmark. Two were while at Aberdeen, the other a 1-0 victory in Copenhagen after his move to Hibs. Harper would be one of several Scotland players suspended indefinitely after a fracas outside a nightclub after the game. The suspensions however would later be lifted and Harper would make one other appearance for his country when replacing Kenny Dalglish in the second-half of a 1-1 draw with Iran during Scotland's ill-fated World Cup campaign in Argentina in 1978, but by this time he had returned to Aberdeen.

20 John Collins scored from a direct free-kick in the 2-2 draw.

7 A NEW BEGINNING

1 That same afternoon at Ibrox in a game against Rangers, the Celtic and Scotland goalkeeper John Thomson would be seriously injured after courageously diving at the feet of an opponent and would die from his injuries later that evening.

2 Harry Swan became the first non-Catholic to sit on the board of Hibernian Football Club.

3 With the team failing to gain promotion at the first time of asking Swan resigned accusing his fellow directors of lacking ambition.

4 With Hibs now in the Second Division, that season's New Year's Day game was against St Bernard's at the Gymnasium, the home side winning 1-0.

5 When Harry Swan first became chairman, Hibs games usually kicked-off at 3.15pm, allegedly to allow the publicans in the area more time to sell their wares although this was a common practice that took place in many parts of the country at that time. In those days most men worked on Saturday mornings, often till one o'clock, but after complaints from the newspaper reporters who struggled to get their match reports out in time for the Saturday evening sports editions, Swan soon made sure that the kick-off times reverted back to the traditional 3.00pm.

6 Capped 33 times for Canada, defender Paul Fenwick would make 84 league appearances for the Easter Road side between 2000–2004.

7 Three. Hibs, St Bernard's and Edinburgh City. Leith Athletic would finish the campaign at the foot of the First Division and would themselves be relegated leaving Hearts as the city's only representative in the top division the following season.

8 Peter Carruthers was father of Eric Carruthers who played for

7

Hearts during Hibs 7-0 victory at Tynecastle day 1973. Peter himself had played a few games for the Gorgie side in the late 1920s.

9 The long serving director Barney Lester was owner of the Albion Bar that was situated at the corner of Albion Road and Albion Place and is now a shop.

10 After changing from the green and white hooped jerseys around 1879, the strips remained plain all green with only the occasional change to the collars throughout the years. In 1933 a white collar was added to the jersey for the very first time.

11 After a 8-3 league defeat by Hearts at Tynecastle on 21 September in 1935, two prominent Hibs players Willie Watson and Duncan Urquhart were accused of having played under the influence of alcohol, many of the irate Hibs supporters claiming that on a couple of occasions Watson had been seen throwing up behind the goals. Although Urquhart had played for the full Scotland side against Wales in 1934 and Watson for the Scottish League that same season, both would shortly be given free transfers, Watson who had been at Hibs for six seasons, joining Ayr United and Urquhart signing for Aberdeen after eight seasons at Easter Road.

12 Willie Finnigan, who would win a championship medal with the club in 1948. A part-time footballer, Finnigan would work during the week in the St Cuthbert's Cooperative warehouse in Nicolson Street.

13 A contract mix-up between Dundee United and Liverpool over the loan of the player allowed Hibs to step in and sign Milne. Hibs would later be fined over the affair but allowed to retain the player who would spend the following ten seasons at Easter Road before joining St Mirren in a £2,500 deal in 1947.

14 In the first round of the 1938 Scottish Cup competition Hibs had been drawn away against Edinburgh City who were then rooted firmly at the foot of the Second Division. In an effort to generate

more revenue, the lower league side had agreed to switch the tie from their home ground at City Park to Easter Road. Incredibly, Hibs would be defeated 3-2 by the rank outsiders, even managing to miss a penalty much to the embarrassment and fury of their supporters. It was also a bad day for Hibs great rivals Hearts who lost to Second Division Dundee United at Tannadice that same afternoon.

15 Signed during the 1938–39 season Gerry Mays would be a registered Hibs player throughout the Second World War although making few appearances presumably as he would be serving in the armed forces. Transferred to St Johnstone in 1947 he joined Dunfermline the following season. In a League Cup semi-final between Hibs and Second Division Dunfermline at Tynecastle in 1949, Mays scored twice against his former side in a 2-1 extra-time victory. As a result of the defeat, Hibs midfield trio who had been performing poorly for some time would be completely changed for the next game against Queen of the South at Easter Road. As part of the reorganisation Bobby Combe would be moved back to left-half and replaced in the forward line by Bobby Johnstone, permanently as it would turn out. It would be the first ever outing in a competitive game as a complete unit of the Famous Five.

16 Hibs famous white sleeves were first worn in a home league game against Hamilton Academicals on 13 August 1938, the game ending in a 2-2 draw. The idea of white sleeves had apparently been influenced by Arsenal, but Arsenal themselves claim that it had originally been suggested to the Chelsea director Joe Mears who rejected the idea, and it was quickly adopted by the Arsenal manager Herbert Chapman who felt that the white sleeves would make it easier for his players to find each other.

17 Winning his only cap in Scotland's 3-2 defeat of Wales at Tynecastle in November 1938 goalkeeper Jock Brown would also win a Scottish Cup winners medal in Clyde's 4-0 victory over Motherwell in the 1939 final. Signing for Hibs in 1946 he made around a dozen appearances for the league side until joining Dundee during the

7

1947–48 season. Later physio to the Scottish Rugby side, he was the father of the famous rugby players Gordon and Peter.

18 The impeccably dressed McCartney would rarely be seen without either a Bowler or Homburg hat or a carnation in his buttonhole.

19 10th at the end of the 1937–38 season.

20 The game, to commemorate the Coronation of George VI at Westminster that same day ended 2-0 in the Glasgow sides favour.

8   BEHIND THE SCENES

1   Philip Farmer, a great uncle of the present Hibs owner Sir Tom Farmer.

2   The former Celtic centre forward Jimmy McColl who joined Hibs from Partick Thistle in 1922 and would go on to give the club over 50 years service until his death in 1978 aged 86 scored over 100 goals for both clubs.

3   Hibs had not long been promoted from the second division when Swan made what many thought to be a rash promise when he was reported as saying: 'Give me ten years and I will make this club great again.' He would be out by only a few years but in the end it would be a promise fulfilled.

4   Harry Reading who along with his Easter Road duties also helped to run the successful juvenile side Edinburgh Thistle and would recommend many players to Hibs including Lawrie Reilly and Archie Buchanan.

8

5   In 1949 the programme editor Magnus Williamson was asked to create the best programme in the entire country. At that time programmes were usually flimsy four page issues comprising mainly of the team line-ups and adverts. Magnusson's programme however was revolutionary for that time. Larger in format than before, the most prominent feature of the eight- and sometimes 12-page editions was the large black and white photo on the front cover. Inside there would be numerous items of interest and the player's line-up in team formation. At thruppence it was a penny dearer than before but was a huge hit with the supporters and sold in large numbers.

6   Between the years 1952–1956 Harry Swan was President of the SFA.

7   A player at Easter Road between 1954 and 1965, after a short spell with Stenhousemuir John Fraser would become trainer to the

Turnbull's Tornadoes in the 1970s and would give the club more than 25 years loyal service.

8   During the halcyon post-war years Swan would be joined on the Hibs board by the retired businessman Tom Hartland and Lawyer Wilson Terris. Later the long serving secretary Ken McIntyre would also be made a director.

9   Officially formed on 1 May 1946 the Hibernian Supporters Association had several individual branches throughout the city and beyond, holding meetings at many different locations. Later, after purchasing premises at 7 Carlton Terrace the official opening of the supporters club, the first venture of its kind in the country, took place on 29 June 1955. Comprising of a public bar, function room and games room it also had limited overnight accommodation for travelling Hibs fans. Popular with the supporters it would remain in use until the present clubrooms at Sunnyside were opened in 1965.

10 The long serving Hibs player Sammy Kean who had joined Hibs in 1937 became trainer at Easter Road in the 1950s but had joined the future Hibs manager Bob Shankly at Dundee when the Dens Park side won the league championship for the very first time in 1962.

11 Hibs home game against Hearts on 20 September 1952, Lawrie Reilly scoring a hat-trick in a 3-1 victory for the home side, was the first game to be transmitted live to several hospitals in the Edinburgh area by the recently formed Hospital Radio Organisation. Run by volunteers, in time the service would be extended to cover games at Tynecastle and would eventually be received by over a dozen hospitals.

12 In 1963 Harry Swan sold the club to the prominent Edinburgh businessman William Harrower who owned around 50 betting shops and numerous other properties around the city although Swan would remain on the board as a reward for his tremendous service to the club.

13 In 1963 the former Third Lanark physiotherapist Tom McNiven joined the club. The popular McNiven had actually agreed to join Morton when he became aware of Hibs interest and luckily for a generation of Hibs players Morton had agreed not to stand in the way of his move to Edinburgh. Later a valued member of the Scotland backroom staff, apart from a short break in the late 1970s he would serve the club well for almost 20 years.

14 When Jock Stein joined Hibs from Dunfermline in 1964 he brought along with him trainer Jimmy Stevenson. Stevenson however would remain at Easter Road after Stein's premature move to join Celtic shortly after, and would later return to Dunfermline.

15 The former Motherwell player Wilson Humphries had been part of the Motherwell side that defeated Hibs in the 1950 League Final and also a member of the Scottish Cup winning team against Celtic in 1952. The former schoolteacher had earlier been manager of St Mirren but had left Love Street after the side had been relegated to return to teaching and was a surprise appointment when he joined Hibs as part of Turnbull's backroom staff at the start of the 1972 season.

16 The well equipped Civil Service Sports Complex at Silverknowes.

17 Sir John Bruce who had been knighted for his services to medicine in 1963 was a former Hibs chairman and president of the Royal College of Surgeons in Edinburgh. Seriously injured in a car accident in the city, it would appear that he had never fully recovered from his injuries and died in the Western General Hospital in December 1975 aged 70.

18 Discontinued for financial reasons in the mid-1950s, in 1971 chairman Tom Hart resurrected the Hibs third team. Overseen by the former Hibs player Stan Vincent the side would once again play in the East of Scotland League, their home games played at City Park.

19 A consortium of Edinburgh businessmen, thought to be members
    of the private Hibs 50 Club who were said to be dissatisfied at
    Tom Harts running of the club were rumoured to have offered to
    purchase the chairman's shares. Replying to what he called 'faceless
    people that refused to identify themselves' Hart announced that he
    was not prepared to deal with anyone that was not prepared to show
    their hand in public, and the matter was at an end.

20 After Pat Stanton had replaced Bertie Auld as manager at Easter
    Road in 1982, the former players George Stewart and Jimmy
    O'Rourke had been brought in as part of the new manager's
    backroom staff.

9   THE SECOND WORLD WAR

1   Five, winning just two and losing three before play was suspended.

2   The 5-3 defeat by Albion Rovers at Easter Road on 2 September 1939 would be Hibs final peacetime game before the Second World War, Sammy Kean scoring the Easter Road side's last goal before the lights went out on official football for several years. Hibs other goal scorers that day were Nutley and McLean.

3   During the Second World War Scottish players were allowed to earn £2 per game excluding bonuses which was 10/- (50p more than their counterparts down south). This made playing in Scotland more lucrative particularly for those serving in the forces or on war related occupations often in the north of England.

4   On New Year's Day 1940 the game between Hibs and Hearts ended 6-5 in favour of the away side. What made a game that in all probability should really have been cancelled unusual, is that it took place under a thick blanket of fog that made it almost impossible for those inside the ground to follow play. Because wartime regulations prohibited any mention of inclement weather over the country that could have alerted enemy forces, the well-known radio commentator Rex Kingsley of the *Sunday Mail* was forced to broadcast the entire second half with a coherent but entirely fictitious commentary of a game he could not see, only being kept up to date with the score and scorers by runners in the crowd. Hibs had been leading 2-1 at half-time when the referee, realising he had called a halt two minutes early, called the players back to complete the two minutes during which time Hearts scored twice to take a 3-2 lead.

5   In the dressing room after the game the Hearts outside right Donaldson was found to be missing. Completely unaware that the game had ended a 'search party' would later find the player still at his station peering into the murky gloom.

6   In the first season of the war the leagues had been split into East
     and West sections, an arrangement that obviously meant no money
     spinning games against the 'Old Firm' for sides from the east, several
     posting financial losses. Hibs threat to go into voluntary liquidation
     would go some way towards the league system being changed the
     following season into the Southern and North Eastern Leagues 1 and
     2 which now gave the likes of Hibs and Hearts the lucrative games
     against the 'Old Firm'.

7   Stationed at nearby Dalmahoy, the Bishop Auckland player Hardisty
     had joined Hibs as a guest during the 1941–42 season, the signing
     initially creating a major problem for the club when they had
     difficulty finding boots to fit his unusually large feet. Hardisty went
     on to make 18 appearances for the Easter Road side but is probably
     best remembered for his tremendous post-war amateur career,
     winning the FA Amateur Cup three times at Wembley with Bishop
     Auckland in the 1950s. He was also a member of the Amateur
     England side that took part in the 1948, 1952 and 1956 Olympic
     Games.

8   Then still a registered Everton player Jimmy Caskie and another
     guest player had been fined and banned from playing for St Mirren
     after being found guilty of receiving illegal under the counter
     payments. Several of the clubs directors would be banned from the
     game indefinitely. Caskie would go on to represent Hibs many times
     as a guest between 1941–1945 while also winning five wartime
     Scotland caps. Transferred to Rangers during the 1946–47 season,
     his first game for the Ibrox side would be a 2-1 defeat by Hibs in
     Glasgow.

9   Hibs defeated Rangers 3-2 at Hampden in the inaugural Harry Swan
     inspired Summer Cup, Willie Finnigan scoring twice, once from the
     penalty spot, the winning goal scored late in the game by centre half
     Bobby Baxter. It is said that with the scores level and time running
     out the tension became too unbearable for the Hibs manager Willie
     McCartney who spent the final few minutes pacing nervously behind
     the Hampden stand.

10 Bobby Combe scored four goals in Hibs 8-1 victory against Rangers at Easter Road on 27 September 1941. Although it was classed as an unofficial wartime fixture, the comprehensive victory remains the Ibrox sides heaviest ever defeat in a competitive game.

11 Smith worked at Robb's Shipyard in Leith and would later be joined by team mate Bobby Combe for a short while until the latter was called up for military service.

12 Under wartime regulations it had earlier been decided that no extra time would be played in Hibs Summer Cup Final against Rangers at Hampden in 1942. With the scores still level at 0-0 after 90 minutes Rangers were declared the winners on the toss of a coin.

13 Matt Busby, later manager of Manchester United was an army PT instructor based at Kelso. As a guest player he would make 38 appearances for Hibs between 1941–43 scoring five goals before his move to Shetland with his unit. During his time at Easter Road he would represent Scotland twice in unofficial wartime internationals against England and also make one appearance for the Scottish League side.

14 Before the 1944 Southern League Cup Final between Hibs and Rangers at Hampden it had been decided that in the event of the game ending level after 90 minutes, the side winning the most corners would be declared the winners. After 89 minutes the game still remained goalless and the flag kick tally even when Rangers conceded a corner from a Caskie move to give Hibs the cup by six corners to five.

15 For many years the annual charity game between an Edinburgh Select side and a team from England would act as the precursor to the new season. The games would usually take place between Easter Road and Tynecastle alternately, the players wearing the home side's colours and featuring six players from the home side and five from the other, although for the first couple of games visiting players had been allowed. The series that ran for 18 seasons from

9

1944 would often attract gates of more than 40,000 but by the 1960s it was capable of drawing just half that number and the series was gradually allowed to drop. The last, at least in the meantime, was a game against Burnley at Tynecastle in 1962. In 1985 the Edinburgh Select was briefly resurrected with a game against Bayern Munich at Tynecastle the sides competing for the Festival Cup. The Meadowbank Thistle player Alan Lawrence had included in the home line up, but despite reported intentions at the time to continue the fixture, no further games have ever taken place.

16   The entire Scottish forward line comprising of Smith, Milne and Caskie of Hibs and Walker and Black of Hearts had all been signed by manager Willie McCartney at one time or another. The centre half that afternoon was Bobby Baxter of Hibs who had also been signed by McCartney. It was also said to have been the first time that a Scotland side had worn numbers on their jerseys.

17   The great Bill Shankly, then still a registered player with Preston North End and later manager of Liverpool, lined up for Partick that afternoon at Hampden in a 2-0 victory over Hibs. He was joined in the Thistle side by a soon to be Hearts stalwart Bobby Parker

18   Although failing to make many appearances, the father of the Hibs captain of the 1991 Skol Cup winning side Murdo McLeod, also named Murdo, was a registered Hibs player between 1937–1942.

19   Hibs last official wartime league game was a 4-2 victory over Queens Park at Hampden on 23 April 1946 and only a couple of weeks before Hitler's suicide in the Berlin bunker. Hibs goalscorers that afternoon were Smith (2 Kean and Milne.

20   After Germany's surrender in May 1945 the war still continued against the Japanese in the Far East. Japan would eventually announce its surrender in August 1945 but would not formally come into operation until 2 September. Because a few games had already taken place it was decided to continue the 1945–46 season as an unofficial wartime league.

10 GORDON SMITH

1   Smith spent the majority of his early years in the Angus market town of Montrose where his father worked in a local grocers shop.

2   On both occasions he lined up against the England and Ireland schoolboy sides alongside his future Hibs team mate Bobby Combe.

3   Smith was signed from junior side Dundee North End in 1941. He first came to the clubs attention when scoring a hat trick for a Junior XI against a Hearts/Hibs select in a game to officially open Lochee United's Beechwood Park.

4   Bomb damage on the line meant that the train carrying the Hibs manager and chairman to Smith's home in Montrose could go no further and the signing was completed in an Arbroath hotel.

5   Willie McCartney was the Hibs manager who signed Smith in April 1941.

6   Gordon Smith made his debut for Hibs a few days short of his 17th birthday wearing borrowed boots in a game against Hearts at Tynecastle on 28th April 1941 that had been postponed from New Year, scoring a hat-trick in Hibs 5-3 victory. The other Hibs goals were scored by Combe and Adams. The future Hearts manager Tommy Walker scored all three of the home sides goals.

7   Smith made his international debut at Wembley in October 1944 in England's 6-2 victory, although the game would be classed as an unofficial wartime international.

8   Throughout his Scotland career Smith would often compete with Rangers Willie Waddell for a place in the international side. Waddell would win 17 full caps for Scotland not counting wartime internationals compared to Smith's 18 plus another three that were classed as unofficial wartime games. (*The wartime game against

10

Belgium in 1946 has now been recognised as official making the total 19. He also played nine times for the Scottish League.)

9   By scoring five goals from the outside right position in Hibs 8-0 victory over Third Lanark on 8 November 1947 Gordon Smith equalled the goal scoring record by a wide player in an official game. The record would not be broken until April 1959 when Harry Melrose scored six in Dunfermline's 10-1 victory against Partick Thistle.

10 The roadhouse was aptly named 'The Right Wing.'

11 Smith featured in five of Hibs inaugural European Cup games during the 1955–56 season. Delayed by fog after a Scottish representative game in Denmark along with Lawrie Reilly and goalkeeper Tommy Younger he would miss the home game against Rot Weiss of Essen when their plane was delayed by fog. He failed to score in any of the games.

12 He scored his 300th goal for the club in a 3-0 home win against Aberdeen on Saturday 27 December 1952. The goal was recorded for posterity on an 8-inch disc and is currently on display at Easter Road. Hibs other goals that afternoon were scored by Lawrie Reilly and Willie Ormond.

13 Four. Outside right, centre forward, outside left and once at inside right to Rangers Willie Waddell in a game against Wales in 1945 which was classed as an unofficial wartime fixture.

14 In 1951 Gordon Smith was presented with the Scottish Sports Writers Player of the Year award at a ceremony in the Waverley Market in Edinburgh.

15 Only two. Willie McCartney and Hugh Shaw.

16 Smith made a farewell to the international scene when scoring Scotland's solitary goal in a 4-1 defeat by Spain at the Bernabeu

stadium in a World Cup qualifier on 26 May 1957.

17 The Brazilian side Vasco de Gama were rumoured to have tried to sign both Smith and Bobby Johnstone after the clubs trip to the South American country in the summer of 1953.

18 In total Smith scored 364 goals for Hibs in all games including unofficial wartime matches.

19 As well as collecting a league championship medal with Hearts at the end of the 1959–60 season, he would also win his first cup medal in senior football in Hearts 2-1 victory over Third Lanark in the 1959 League Cup Final.

20 After winning three league championship medals with Hibs between 1948–52, Hearts 1960 and Dundee 1962, Smith would spend a short period with Morton during which time he failed to play any games, finally ending an illustrious playing career with the Irish side Drumcondra in 1965 aged almost 40.

_10_

II THE FAMOUS FIVE

1   Eddie Turnbull made his competitive debut for the first team in a
    league cup tie against Third Lanark at Hampden (Cathkin at that
    time was unavailable on Saturday 26 October 1946. Man-of-the-
    match Turnbull would set up the first goal for Gordon Smith in
    Hibs 2-1 victory before scoring the winner himself. He had actually
    made his first full appearance at Easter Road 11 days earlier in Hibs
    friendly match against AC Sparta. His league debut came seven days
    after the League Cup game in Hibs 4-1 victory over Third Lanark
    at Easter Road, the Hibs goals this time scored by Turnbull (2
    Buchanan and Weir.

2   Willie Ormond was signed from Stenhousemuir in 1946 for a fee
    said to be in the region of £2,500 after prolonged negotiations
    lasting well into the night.

3   On 15 October 1949 goals from Gordon Smith and Eddie Turnbull
    gave Hibs a comfortable 2-0 home win against Queen of the
    South. Although the five had appeared together against Nithsdale
    Wanderers in a friendly at Sanquhar and also in a game against an
    Irish League XI in Belfast in friendly games the previous season, the
    game against Queen of the South was the very first appearance of
    the Famous Five as a complete unit in a competitive match. The Hibs
    line up that afternoon was: Younger, Govan and Cairns, Combe
    Paterson and Buchanan, Smith Johnstone Reilly Turnbull and
    Ormond.

4   Gordon Smith with 25 league goals, 29 in all games. Smith had been
    Hibs top league goal scorer in seven of the previous eight seasons,
    however Lawrie Reilly would top the list for the next seven years,
    including three consecutive seasons as the top goalscorer in Scotland
    until the arrival of Joe Baker in 1957–58.

5   Goalkeeper Tommy Younger had been injured just before half time
    leaving Hibs to play the entire second half with just ten men. Eddie

Turnbull had been expected to take over in goals but surprisingly the position was handed to full-back Willie Clarke leaving Turnbull to score all four Hibs goals in the 4-1 victory. Three of the goals were scored from the penalty spot, a feat unequalled in Scotland at that time, the other a trademark thunderous drive. Celtic's goal scored by Bobby Collins also came from the penalty spot after a retake. Ironically Collins himself would later score three times for Celtic from the spot in a game against Aberdeen in 1953.

6   Lawrie Reilly was the only one of the Famous Five to support the club as a youngster.

7   The 1-0 defeat by Austria at Hampden on 13 December 1950 was Scotland's first ever defeat on home soil by a foreign side. Turnbull would not play for the full side again for nearly eight years.

8   Collectively the Famous Five would win 13 league championship medals between 1948–1952. Smith, Turnbull and Ormond would each win three. Reilly would not make enough appearances during the 1947–48 season to qualify for a medal and Johnstone would not make his debut until 1949, both the latter receiving medals for only the 1951 and 1952 campaigns.

9   Only two. Gordon Smith would receive a testimonial match against Manchester United in 1952, Lawrie Reilly a game between a Hibs XI and an International Select in 1958 by which time he had retired prematurely because of injury. Somewhat absurdly Reilly had not been allowed to play in his own testimonial game because he was not then a registered player.

10 After being refused a testimonial game as had been awarded to Gordon Smith the previous year, at the start of the 1953–54 season the centre-forward went on Strike. With neither side prepared to back down Reilly would miss several games, but with Scotland also missing the player's services the issue was finally settled when the then SFA secretary George Graham offered to arrange a testimonial for the player against a representative side sometime in the future.

Eventually returning to the side, later that season Reilly complained of feeling unwell during a game against Aberdeen and was later diagnosed as suffering from pleurisy and would not play again until the following season.

11 The 3-2 home defeat by Clyde would turn out to be the last ever outing of the Famous Five as a complete unit before Bobby Johnstone's transfer to Manchester City a few weeks later. The Five would all feature the following week in a Scottish Cup tie against Hearts at Tynecastle but by this time Turnbull would be at right-half, his place in the forward line taken by Bobby Combe.

12 When selected for the Home International game against England at Hampden in April 1954, a 4-2 defeat, Willie Ormond became the last of the Five to be capped by Scotland in a full international.

13 None. The nearest all five came to being selected 'en bloc' for Scotland was when Smith, Johnstone, Reilly and Ormond all played for the Scottish League against Eire in a 5-1 victory at Parkhead in September 1952, Lawrie Reilly scoring four of the goals. Dundee's Billy Steele filled the inside left position.

14 On Saturday 15 January 1955 Hibs home game against Queen of the South was the only senior game in Scotland to escape cancellation due to the heavy fall of snow that had badly affected the entire country. Unfortunately, within 21 minutes of the start the game had to be abandoned due to the snow obliterating the lines. At the time Hibs had been leading 3-0 all the goals scored by Johnstone, but because the result did not stand the goals are obviously not included in the official records. Unofficial or not they would be the last goals that Johnstone would score for the club – at least for the moment. When the rearranged game eventually went ahead a few weeks later Johnstone was a Manchester City player.

15 Bobby Combe had been a regular in the forward line until moving back to wing half to accommodate Bobby Johnstone in 1949. After Johnstone's transfer to Manchester City in 1955 Combe would

II

revert back to inside left, Eddie Turnbull filling Johnstone's previous position at inside right, later moving back permanently to right-half.

16 Both Bobby Johnstone and Willie Ormond had been selected for the 1954 World Cup Finals in Switzerland. Johnstone however had been injured while training with the Scotland party leaving Ormond as the only Hibs player to take part in what would be a disastrous competition, the Scots losing 1-0 to Austria before a humiliating 7-0 defeat by Uruguay. Eddie Turnbull was Hibs sole representative in the 1958 Finals in Sweden, although the former Hibs goalkeeper Tommy Younger then with Liverpool captained the side.

17 None, although all five did feature in the 2-0 Coronation Cup final defeat by Celtic at Hampden in 1953.

18 Willie Ormond was the only one of the Five to play all his games for Scotland in the one position, in his case outside left. Smith would feature at outside right, inside right, centre forward and outside left, Reilly at centre forward and both wing positions and Turnbull at inside left and right half. Johnstone would play all his games at inside right except for the game against Norway in 1954 when he had been selected as outside right.

19 Lawrie Reilly remains Hibs top goalscorer to this very day with 234 in all competitions. Gordon Smith has actually scored more but many of his 364 goals would be scored during what were classed as unofficial wartime fixtures.

20 Gordon Smith was the first to arrive at Easter Road in 1941 followed by Lawrie Reilly in 1944. Eddie Turnbull was signed in 1946 closely followed by Willie Ormond. Bobby Johnstone was signed that same year although he would spend a couple of years in first the third team, then the reserves, before making a breakthrough into the first team in 1949. Ormond would be the last of the Five to leave as a player when joining home town team Falkirk in 1961 although Turnbull was then still on the books as trainer.

12 BEHIND THE FIVE

1   Archie Buchanan who would win three league championship medals
    at Easter Road before a move to St Mirren during the 1956–57
    season.

2   Full-back Davie Shaw who would move to Aberdeen in 1949 and
    later become trainer then manager of the Grampian side.

3   Goalkeeper George Farm would pre date Younger at the juvenile
    side before signing for Hibs. After only a few games for the club
    during the 1947–48 season he was transferred to Blackpool where
    he would collect an FA Cup winners medal in the famous 'Matthews
    Final' against Bolton Wanderers in 1953.

4   Jock Govan, Davie Shaw, Bobby Combe, Gordon Smith and Eddie
    Turnbull had all been selected in the Scotland side to face Belgium
    at Hampden in April 1948 and also the game against Switzerland in
    Berne a few weeks later. Hibs defender Hugh Howie was selected as
    travelling reserve for the game against Belgium.

5   All three were different nationalities. Archie Buchanan Scottish, John
    Paterson English and Michael Gallagher Irish.

6   The Easter Road full-backs Jock Govan and Davie Shaw would
    represent Scotland as a defensive pairing on five occasions in 1948
    and only Govan's illness would prevent them from both appearing
    together against Wales a few months later.

7   Winning a League Championship medal with Hibs in 1951,
    Irishman Michael Gallagher who had been signed from Alloa in
    1948 would represent Eire against Luxembourg in March 1954
    before a move to Ayr United along with team mate Jock Govan at
    the start of the 1954–55 season.

8   The highly rated defender John Ogilvie, who had only just made the

break through into the first team, would break his leg in two places during the semi-final against Motherwell at Tynecastle in 1951 and would be out of the game for over a year. The injury would severely limit his first team opportunities at Easter Road and he would later spend four seasons with Leicester City before ending his playing career with Mansfield Town.

9   The game against Clyde would be one of only a handful of appearances Jim Souness would make for the first team. A registration mix-up between Hibs and Falkirk after a loan spell Brockville would later allow him to join Hearts with whom he would win a League Cup medal in 1954.

10 Left-back Jimmy Cairns who broke his leg in a game against Rangers in a league game at Ibrox near the end of the 1949–50 season but managed to finish the game. Completely unaware that the leg had been broken, the true extent of the injury was only discovered several days later.

11 Equally comfortable at centre-half or left-back John Paterson, father of Craig, would spend 13 seasons at Easter Road, many playing behind the Famous Five before a move to Ayr United in 1959.

12 A pre-war signing, right back Willie Clark would make only eight appearances for the club during the war years presumably because he was serving in the armed forces at the time. In the immediate post-war years he encountered great difficulty in forcing himself into the first team because of the consistency of the Scotland full-back Jock Govan and he would eventually join St Johnstone in time for the start of the 1953–54 season.

13 Tommy McQueen father of the more famous Gordon McQueen.

14 Jimmy 'Tiger' Thomson, earned the nickname because of his wholehearted approach to the game. The trio of Thomson, Plenderleith and Preston that lined up in the first ever European Cup games against Rot Weiss of Essen and Djurgaardens in 1955

was said at that time to have been the youngest half back line in the entire country.

15 Centre-half Jackie Plenderleith.

16 Although a bit on the slow side Tommy Preston was a clever player with a tremendous football brain and deft touch. He would later move back to left half, scoring in both Fairs Cup games against Barcelona, and would serve the club well for ten seasons before an ill-fated move to St Mirren in 1964.

17 Signed from Tranent Juniors, as well as the Rot Weiss game full-back Willie MacFarlane would also feature in both legs against Djurgaardens and Stade Reims as Hibs went all the way to the semi-finals of the competition. Later after a move to Raith Rovers he would manage several East-of-Scotland sides and Stirling Albion before taking over as manager at Easter Road in 1968.

18 Spending a large part of his National Service based in Germany goalkeeper Tommy Younger is said to have been flown back to Scotland on more than 70 occasions to play for Hibs. He would later be presented with a commemorative plaque by the airline company in recognition of the feat.

19 After signing for the club in 1954 John Grant would go on to give Hibs ten years service. Capped for Scotland against Wales and Northern Ireland in 1958, he would later join Raith Rovers.

20 Musselburgh born Doug Moran scored the winning goal for Falkirk in the replayed Scottish Cup final against Kilmarnock in 1957 while on loan from Hibs. He would sign for the Brockville side at the end of the season but at the time of the cup final he was still registered to Easter Road so technically before Hibs Scottish Cup win in 2016 Moran had been the last Hibs player to score the winning goal in a Scottish Cup Final.

12

13 LAWRIE REILLY

1   While still a schoolboy Reilly joined the well known juvenile side
    Edinburgh Thistle then run by the Hibs groundsman Harry Reading,
    scoring 106 goals in 55 games from the centre forward position.
    Hearts had reputedly been keen to sign the player but there was only
    going to be one destination for the Hibs mad youngster and that was
    Easter Road.

2   It is said that after a game between Hearts and Hibs at Tynecastle
    one day the young Reilly met Gordon Smith in the street and invited
    the player up to his house for tea. Smith turned down the offer, but
    in the near future he would later regularly visit the house as a team
    mate.

3   Reilly's dad John worked on the railways and both he and his son
    would take full advantage of the free travel passes to follow Hibs
    around the country.

4   He was an apprentice painter and decorator.

5   He made his full debut for Scotland at centre forward in a 3-1 defeat
    of Wales at Ninian Park in October 1948. Although he would play
    in several different positions throughout the years, several at outside-
    left most of his 38 games for Scotland would be in the centre-
    forward position.

6   Reilly's first hat-trick in senior football, the first of several that
    he would score for Hibs, came during a 6-0 home victory against
    Queen of the South on 11 October 1947. Hibs other goalscorers that
    day were Ormond, Combe and Turnbull.

7   Conscription, or National service had been introduced in 1947 for
    men between the ages of 18 and 26 unless in full-time education or
    learning a trade, and remained in place until the end of the 1950s.
    Initially exempt because of his trade as a painter and decorator,

13

Reilly would have expected his call up papers at the end of his apprenticeship only to discover that because of the excessive number of inductees that year, anyone born in the month of October 1928 would be exempt. Team mate Archie Buchanan who was born just 24 days before Reilly would also take advantage of the situation.

8 Although Reilly would score several last minute goals throughout his career he would earn the nickname 'Last Minute Reilly' when scoring the second of his two goals that afternoon in the very last minute of the 2-2 draw with England at Wembley in 1953.

9 Reilly holds the record for the number of caps won by a Hibs player, scoring 22 goals in 38 appearances for the full Scotland side. He would also make 13 appearances for the Scottish League scoring 14 times.

10 His name was originally to have been the accepted spelling of Lawrence but the registrar made a mistake on the birth certificate, and Lawrance it remained.

11 Returning from a self imposed exile in 1953 he made his first team come back against Manchester United at Old Trafford in a benefit match for United's long serving trainer Tom Curry, scoring both goal in a 2-2 draw. Unfortunately, in 1958 Curry would lose his life in the Munich Air Disaster.

12 Gordon Smith, Tommy Younger and Lawrie Reilly had all been selected for Scotland's game against a Denmark XI in Copenhagen, the countries first ever game under floodlights. Reilly however had been injured during a training session and did not play. However, thick fog at the airport had delayed their flight back to Scotland and they were unable to make it to Easter Road in time for the game against Rot Weiss.

13 Reilly's 38th and last appearance for Scotland was a 1-0 defeat by England at Wembley on 6 April 1957, lining up that afternoon in

direct opposition to the equally famous England centre half Billy Wright.

14 Lawrie Reilly has scored more goals against England than any other Scottish player, five in four consecutive games at Wembley, 1949, 1951, 1953, and 1955. He also scored Scotland's goal in a 2-1 defeat by England at Hampden in 1952.

15 The most number of goals scored by Reilly in a single game is four, once in a league game against Falkirk at Easter Road on 9 September 1950 and again against Motherwell at Fir Park on 27 September 1952.

16 Reilly's last game before retirement was against Rangers at Easter Road on Monday 22 April 1958, just a few days before Hibs faced Clyde in that year's Scottish Cup Final, Reilly scoring one of the goals in a 3-1 victory against his old adversaries. Hibs other goals were scored by Fraser and Baxter. At the final whistle the players of both sides formed a guard of honour to applaud Reilly from the field in recognition of his tremendous career.

17 Reilly became Hibs most capped player ever in Scotland's 5-0 victory against Belgium in Brussels on 20 May 1951, his 12 appearances for the national side beating goalkeeper Harry Rennie's previous record of 11 at the beginning of the century.

18 Reilly swallowed a mouthful of what can only be described as putrid water while swimming in the sea just a few days before Hibs game against Botafogo in Brazil and had spent some time in hospital. He would go straight to the game from his sick bed, scoring Hibs solitary goal in the 3-1 defeat.

19 A few years before his retirement Reilly had opened the Bowlers Rest public house at Elbe Street in Leith which was always a popular destination for fans attending games at Easter Road. After his retirement he would now spend his time either behind the bar or continuing with his other passion apart from Hibs, golf.

13

20 Lawrie Reilly was the only one of his forward line colleagues to remain with the one club for his entire career, either as a player, coach or manager.

I4   THE LEAGUE CUP

1   Hibs first ever game in the new league cup competition was a 4-2
    victory against Celtic at Easter Road on 21 September 1946, the
    goals scored by Johnny Aitkenhead, Jock Weir, John Cuthbertson
    and Archie Buchanan. The former Hibs player Tommy Bogan scored
    one of the Celtic goals.

2   In a game against Dundee at Dens Park in 1950 Hibs were leading
    2-0 when the game was cancelled due to the pitch becoming
    waterlogged. With it being the last game in a section already won by
    the Easter Road side it was felt unnecessary to replay the game.

3   Eddie Turnbull scored all three Hibs goals in an eventual 3-1 victory,
    one from the penalty spot to earn his side their first ever appearance
    in a League Cup Final.

4   Motherwell defeated Hibs 3-0 in the 1950 League Cup final only
    two weeks after losing 6-2 at home to an Easter Road side that had
    played most of the game with only ten fit men after Gordon Smith
    had been injured. Goalkeeper Tommy Younger who had been badly
    at fault for at least two of the goals in the final famously burst into
    tears at the final whistle.

5   In the 1959 competition Hibs were leading Motherwell 1-0 with
    only 20 minutes left to play when the Motherwell centre forward
    Ian St John scored a hat-trick in just two and a half minutes to win
    the game for his side. It remains to this day the fastest hat-trick in
    Scottish football.

6   In 1964 Hibs lost 1-0 to Second Division Morton at Hampden
    after a replay, the first game ending 1-1 the future Hibs player Alan
    McGraw scoring in both games for the Cappielow side. Neil Martin
    had scored Hibs goal in the earlier 1-1 draw but would miss the
    replay after breaking his wrist during the game.

I4

7   Hibs highest ever score in a league cup game is 11-2 against Alloa
    at Easter Road in the quarter finals of the competition in 1965, the
    final aggregate score 13-2. Jim Scott and Neil Martin both scored
    four, Quinn, Stevenson and Davis from the penalty spot completing
    the rout.

8   With the Hibs substitute already used, the injured Alan McGraw
    was forced to leave the field for treatment leaving Hibs to play on
    with ten men. He returned a few minutes from full time with his leg
    heavily bandaged, but barely able to move, he somehow managed
    to bundle the ball over the line from a last minute corner, the goal
    sending Hibs through to the clubs second League Cup Final, and
    their first for 18 years.

9   A major fire at Hampden just days before the 1968 final had caused
    extensive damage to the main stand had meant the game having to
    be postponed. At that time Hibs had been playing well, but when the
    final eventually took place a few months later their form had dipped
    somewhat and they would be defeated 6-2 by Celtic.

10 John McNamee was sent off during Celtic's eventual 4-0 victory
    after heatedly disputing a decision by referee Davidson. At first
    refusing to leave the field, for a time it appeared as though the burly
    centre-half was about to attack the official until he was ushered
    away by his team mates, kicking the dug-out as he was going down
    the tunnel. It would also turn out to be Neil Martin's last ever game
    for the club.

11 A new format had been introduced for the 1972 competition. Now
    for the first time sides from the lower division would be included
    in the same sections as teams from the top league. Also, the top
    two from each section would now qualify for the later stages of the
    competition as opposed to just the one as before.

12 With the scores level at 0-0 and extra time looming, after a lung
    bursting 40 yard run through the centre of the Rangers defence from
    just inside his opponents half, John Brownlie fired a tremendous shot

past the Rangers goalkeeper Peter McCloy for the only goal of the game to send his side into the League Cup Final.

13 Hibs first game in the 1991 Skol Cup competition was a 3-0 away victory against Stirling Albion. However because Annfield had an artificial pitch which was not allowed in the competition at that time the game was played at St Johnstone's McDairmid Park in Perth.

14 Signed from Luton just before the final, the former Dundee United player David Beaumont was an unused substitute in the final, winning a medal before he had even kicked a ball for the first team.

15 The Hibs goalkeeper at Hampden that evening was the eccentric man-of-many-clubs John Burridge, Keith Wright scoring the only goal of the game in the first half to send Hibs into the Final.

16 A 1-0 defeat by Second Division Ayr United in the semi-final at Hampden in the 2002 competition would signal the beginning of the end for manager Franck Sauzee at Easter Road. Captaining the Ayr side that evening was the former Hibs player and future manager John Hughes who lined up alongside the former Hibs players Paul Lovering and Pat McGinley.

17 Hibs defeated St Johnstone 3-1 at Tynecastle after extra time, the goals scored by Fletcher, Murphy and Benjelloun.

18 Apart from the goalkeeper, Michael Stewart was the only substitute not to be used. The others were Zemmama, McCann and Martis.

19 Hibs defeated St Johnstone in the 2016 semi final at Tynecastle with goals from Jason Cummings from the penalty spot and John McGinn.

20 Ten. 1950, 1969, 1972, 1974, 1985, 1991, 1992, 2004, 2007 and 2016, winning three, against Celtic in 1972, Dunfermline in 1991 and Kilmarnock in 2007.

14

15 HIBS AND HEARTS

1   After a short period playing their home games at Mayfield Hibs
    would move to a ground at Powderhall (now the site of the council
    incinerator. However, before moving to what would be the first
    Easter Road ground in 1880 they would temporarily return to
    Mayfield, Hearts taking over the lease of the ground at Powderhall.

2   In 1933 a Hibs/Hearts select faced a Rangers/Celtic xi to raise funds
    for the dependants of the eight fishermen from the Granton trawler
    Succession who lost their lives on 19 March 1933 when their boat
    sank after a collision with the Liverpool tanker Atheltarn during a
    snowstorm more than 100 miles off Aberdeen.

3   Tommy Preston.

4   The 17-year-old Joe Baker, his very first goal for the first team.

5   Signed only at the beginning of the season, a young Alan Gordon
    would score twice against Hibs in one of his very first games for the
    Tynecastle side. He would later score many more goals at Easter
    Road but by this time would be wearing the famous green and white
    of Hibs.

6   Willie Hamilton, who beat the Hearts goalkeeper Jim Cruickshank's
    from a narrow angle near the bye-line for the only goal of the game.
    Sadly the former Sheffield United, Middlesbrough, Hearts, Hibs and
    Aston Villa player Hamilton would die in Canada in 1976 aged only
    39.

7   Jimmy O'Rourke celebrated his 19th birthday by scoring the first of
    his two goals that afternoon after only two minutes. Eric Stevenson
    also scored twice in the 4-0 victory, all the goals scored inside the
    first ten minutes of the game.

8   Pat Quinn scored three in Hibs' 4-1 victory at Tynecastle on 9

September 1967. Hibs other goalscorer that afternoon was Peter Cormack.

9   Willie Pettigrew who would be capped five times for Scotland between 1976–77 while playing for Motherwell was a provisional signing at Easter Road but would leave without playing a game. Later after a short spell with Dundee United he would sign for Hearts, finally ending his playing career with Hamilton in 1985 after two seasons with Morton.

10 Hibs goalscorers that famous afternoon at Tynecastle were Jimmy O'Rourke (2 Alan Gordon (2 Arthur Duncan (2 and Alex Cropley.

11 Four, in 1925–26, 1965–66 and 1967–68.

12 Roy Barry, who would make just over a dozen appearances for the Easter Road side before a move to East Fife.

13 Ralph Callaghan appeared for Hearts in the 3-1 Scottish Cup Final defeat by Rangers in 1976 and for Hibs in the twice replayed cup final defeat by Rangers in 1979.

14 Described at the time as the new George Best, Peter Marinello was transferred to Arsenal from Hibs during the 1969–70 season. Scoring on his Arsenal debut against Manchester United it would be the first of only two league goals he would score during his almost three and a half seasons at Highbury before a move to Portsmouth in 1973. Later, after spells at Motherwell, Fulham and Phoenix Inferno he would sign for Hearts during the 1980-81 season finally ending his playing career in the Junior ranks with Whitburn after a short spell with Partick Thistle.

15 Kenny Miller.

16 Apart from Paatelainen, Hibs other goalscorers were John O'Neill, Russell Latapy and David Zitelli.

17 Lawrie Reilly was the last Hibs player before Paatelainen to score a hat-trick against Hearts at Easter Road in a 3-1 victory in September 1952. Bobby Parker scored Hearts goal from the penalty spot.

18 Inside right Danny Paton with three in Hearts 4-0 victory at Easter Road on 8 September 1962, John Cumming scoring the other. In the Hearts side that afternoon were the future Hibs players Willie Hamilton and goalkeeper Gordon Marshall.

19 Hibs had been leading 3-2 when they were awarded a penalty deep into injury time. From the kick Brebner scored after the ball had come back off the goalkeeper to secure what was thought to be a tremendous victory when incredibly David Weir scored twice within a minute to earn his side a 4-4 draw.

20 The former Grimsby Town centre-half Rob Jones, who would also open the scoring in Hibs 5-1 victory over Kilmarnock in the final at Hampden.

16   HIBS IN EUROPE

1   Eddie Turnbull was the scorer of both the first and the second goals that evening in Hibs eventual 4-0 victory over Rot Weiss of Essen in the inaugural game of the European Cup in 1955. Hibs other goalscorers were Lawrie Reilly and Willie Ormond. In the last seconds of the game Gordon Smith had the ball in the net but the Hibs players left the field after the final whistle not knowing if the goal had been allowed to stand until informed later that the referee had blown the final whistle seconds before the ball had crossed the line.

2   It what would be the first ever competitive European game to take place in Glasgow, Hibs away game against Djurgaardens took place at Partick Thistle's Firhill ground on 23 November 1955 because at that time of year the pitches in Sweden were frozen over.

3   The Frenchman Raymond Kopa would win the European Cup with the Madrid side in 1957, 1958 and 1959.

4   The thick blanket fog that had hung over the city all day made visibility at the game almost impossible, and although the referee had left the decision as late as possible, he finally had no alternative but to cancel the game only hours before the kick-off.

5   Hibs tie against Barcelona was the first time that a Scottish side had competed in the Fairs Cup.

6   With the scores level at 2-2 after a 4-4 draw in the first leg in Spain, Bobby Kinloch's goal from the penalty spot would give Hibs a famous 3-2 victory. The decision to award the home side a penalty after Johnny Macleod had been brought down inside the box was not received particularly well by the Barcelona players who for several minutes refused to play on. Order was eventually restored and Kinloch scored what was to be the winning goal. At that, in scenes unprecedented in Britain, mayhem ensued when the visiting

players began to assault the referee and the far side linesman before turning on the police who had come to the aid of the officials, the game held up for several more minutes. At the final whistle the referee was followed down the tunnel by a contingent of Barcelona players intent on seeking revenge for what they thought, wrongly as it would turn out, decision to award the penalty and until the old main stand was demolished several years ago the imprint of studs could still be clearly seen on the referee's changing room door after the Spanish players had tried to gain access.

7   After a suggestion by the then Hibs trainer Eddie Turnbull, before the game against Roma in Italy both centre forward Joe Baker, who had been identified as the main danger man from the first game at Easter Road and inside forward Bobby Kinloch swapped jerseys to confuse their opponents. The ruse almost worked perfectly. With the Roma defenders concentrating more on the number nine who they assumed to be Baker, the real Baker had scored twice before the home side who by that time were then trailing 3-1 realised they had been tricked. The game eventually finished 3-3 meaning a third game play-off was required which would take place back in Italy.

8   After a 2-2 draw in Edinburgh and a 3-3 draw in Rome, the play-off game took place back in Italy at the end of May, a full month after the end of the Scottish season. With only a few days training before the game the Hibs player's obvious lack of match fitness would be a contributory factor in the embarrassing 6-0 defeat.

9   When making his Hibs debut in a Fairs Cup game against Utrecht at Easter Road in 1962 the 16-year-old O'Rourke became the youngest player at that time to take part in a competitive European game.

10   In November 1968 the former Celtic player Joe McBride scored all his sides goals in a 3-1 victory over Lokomotiv Leipzig at Easter Road to become the first ever Hibs player to score a hat-trick in a competitive European game.

11   At the end of the Fairs Cup game against Hamburg at Easter Road

in 1969 a late Hibs goal in the home sides 2-1 victory meant that the aggregate score over two legs remained level at 2-2. Although it was obvious to almost everyone inside the stadium that the visitors had qualified for the next round on account of the away goals ruling counting double in the event of a draw that had recently been introduced, the referee was about to play extra time only for the other officials to inform the now embarrassed referee that the tie was over.

12 Signed only weeks before, the highly rated 18-year-old Kenny Davidson who had made only two appearances for the reserve side, made not only his European debut but his first ever start for the first team in Hibs 3-2 victory in Sweden.

13 In December 1970 manager Willie MacFarlane was sacked after refusing to obey Chairman Tom Hart's instructions that Joe McBride and Johnny Graham should be dropped for the forthcoming Fairs Cup game against Liverpool, a decision that provoked outright condemnation throughout the country.

14 With Hibs wearing purple jerseys with white collars and cuffs, the 2-1 defeat in Lisbon was, according to manager Eddie Turnbull, probably the best display ever by a Hibs side in Europe.

15 In the Fairs Cup game against Leeds in 1973 captain Pat Stanton missed the first penalty, all the others on both sides scoring from the spot to give Leeds a 5-4 victory. Alex Cropley, John Blackley, Des Bremner and John Hazel all scored for Hibs.

16 Hibs highest ever score in a competitive European game that remains to this day is the 9-1 thrashing of the Norwegian side Rosenberg at Easter Road on 2 October 1974, the Edinburgh side going through to the next round with an aggregate 12-3 victory. The Hibs goalscorers that evening were Harper (2 Munro (2 Cropley (2 Stanton (2 and Gordon.

17 After coming on as second half substitute, the aging but still brilliant

Brazilian player Jose Altafini stole the show, scoring twice in the Italian side's eventual 4-2 victory.

18 Not the best player to have ever appeared at Easter Road but perhaps the most famous is Jean-Marc Bosman. A dispute with his club would later lead to the introduction of the now accepted Bosman ruling.

19 With several hundred Hibs supporters already in the Greek capital the game against Athens had been cancelled in respect of those who had lost their lives in the Twin Towers tragedy in New York just two days before.

20 The Edinburgh sides goal in the 5-1 defeat in Dnipro was scored by Derek Riordan, the game watched by the Hibs manager Tony Mowbray.

17 JOE BAKER

1 Both the Baker brothers had been invited down to London by Chelsea. Gerry actually played a couple of lesser games for the English side, but Joe, homesick, would soon return to Scotland.

2 Baker first came to the attention of Hibs when scoring five goals for Lanarkshire Schoolboys in a game against Edinburgh Schools at Tynecastle.

3 Team mates at Armadale Juniors and Hibs, the Scottish international Johnny MacLeod would join Arsenal just a few weeks after Bakers move to Torino in the summer of 1961. Both players would team up again after Bakers transfer to Arsenal the following year. After leaving Arsenal, MacLeod would spend several seasons with Aston Villa before a move to the Belgian side Mechelen in 1968, finally returning to Scotland for a season with Raith Rovers.

4 Perhaps surprisingly Baker failed to score in the comprehensive victory, Marshall (4 Slavin (3 and Aitken Hibs goalscorers on the day.

5 Baker made his first team debut in a League Cup tie against Airdrie at Broomfield on Wednesday 14 August 1957, but would struggle against the far more experienced centre half Doug Baillie who was soon to join Rangers as Hibs were defeated 4-1.

6 Although Barcelona had defeated Hibs 5-1 during the clubs summer tour of Spain in 1959, Baker had impressed enough for the Spanish side to make what at that time was considered to be a very significant offer for the player, an offer however that had immediately been rejected by the Hibs board.

7 In the second round of that seasons Scottish Cup at Tynecastle, underdogs Hibs defeated the much fancied Hearts 4-3, the 18-year-old Baker scoring all four of his side's goals.

8   At that time both Joe Baker and Brian Clough were vying for the England centre forward position. Although Clough had featured in the previous two games Baker would win his first full cap a few weeks later while Clough would never play for England again. In goals for Middlesbrough that evening was Peter Taylor, Clough's future managerial partner.

9   Facing the 17-year-old Baker in a friendly at Easter Road in 1957, the then Wolves and England centre half Billy Wright had been so impressed with the youngster, that he had contacted the then England manager Walter Winterbottom to inform him that the Hibs player was one to watch.

10 At the time of Hibs 1961 Fairs Cup game against Barcelona at Easter Road Baker was still a part time player working as an apprentice Turner. Arriving by train that evening at the Caledonian Station in the west end of the city to find that there were no taxis to be had, the player had been forced to walk to the game through the dense crowds, arriving at the ground shortly before the kick-off.

11 Although he scored nine goals in Hibs 15-1 Scottish Cup victory over Peebles Rovers in 1961, Baker had failed to emulate or even better brother Gerry's 10 goals for St Mirren against Glasgow University in the same competition the previous year.

12 His last appearance in a Hibs jersey, at least for the time being, was in a 6-0 defeat by Roma in the Fairs Cup semi-final third game play-off in Italy on 27 May 1961.

13 In season 1959–60 Baker scored 42 league goals which is still a club record to this very day.

14 As part of the Baker transfer deal Torino had agreed to play Hibs in a friendly match at Easter Road, and on Monday 16 October 1961 a crowd of over 26,000 saw the home side run out worthy 2-0 winners, both Baker and Denis Law featuring for the Italian side.

15 A late night car crash in Turin when the sports car he was driving failed to take a roundabout almost costing the player his life was probably the final straw. In hospital for some weeks the incident would hasten the end of what had been an extremely unhappy time in Italy.

16 At the start of the 1962–63 season the former Hibs player would become manager Billy Wright's first signing for Arsenal.

17 Already capped eight times for the full England side between 1959 and 1965, Baker had been included in the initial list of 40 players for the forthcoming World Cup Finals in England only to miss out when the squad was eventually whittled down to the final 22.

18 On his debut for Hibs second time around against Eddie Turnbull's Aberdeen at Easter Road in 1971, captain for the day Baker caused quite a stir when he took the field wearing white boots, a fairly unusual innovation at that time.

19 Baker was signed from Sunderland in January 1971 by manager Dave Ewing.

20 Not long recovered from a serious injury that had needed an operation, Baker was still featuring regularly in the first team although sometimes as substitute, and he was stunned to learn on the eve of the Cup Final that he had been freed.

17

18 THE SWINGING '60S

1   Both Joe Baker and Johnny Macleod had left the club in the summer of 1961 but they would soon be replaced at Easter Road by Gerry Baker who had been signed from Manchester City and Ally MacLeod from Blackburn Rovers.

2   Both goalkeeper Ronnie Simpson who had been signed from Newcastle United and the former Rangers player Sammy Baird would make their debut along with Stevenson in a 2-0 defeat by St Johnstone at Muirton Park on 8 October 1961. Baird had already made seven appearances for Scotland between 1956–58 while with Rangers. Simpson, a European Cup winner with Celtic in 1967 would become the oldest ever player to make a debut for Scotland in the famous 3-2 victory against England at Wembley that same year aged almost 37.

3   Peter Cormack had been the first ground staff boy at Hearts since the great Tommy Walker in the 1930s. Unfortunately an incident with a grass cutting machine and the perimeter wall at Tynecastle would mean the end of the youngster's time at Tynecastle and he would be quickly snapped by Hibs.

4   Unsettled at Elland Road, Hibs had agreed to meet Leeds original asking price for the 18-year-old Stirling born Billy Bremner, only for the fee then to be increased out of the Edinburgh clubs reach and Bremner would remain at Leeds to lead the club through their most successful years.

5   The exceptionally bad winter of 1962–63 would see most football clubs without a game for several months. Hibs would play Clyde at Easter Road on 29 December and except for a Scottish Cup tie against Brechin in January would not play again until 9 March.

6   Both Baker and Leishman had been part of the St Mirren side that defeated Aberdeen in the 1959 Scottish Cup, Baker scoring the third

goal in his side's 3-1 victory.

7 Stanton was signed by the former Queen's Park and Clyde player
   Walter Galbraith. Galbraith had previously managed the English
   Fourth Division side Tranmere Rovers before joining Hibs.

8 They were all named Stevenson. Eric (1960–71), Maurice (1962–63),
   Jimmy (1964–67) and trainer Jimmy who had joined Hibs from
   Dunfermline as part of the deal that brought Jock Stein to Easter
   Road in 1964.

9 Left back Joe Davis was signed from Third Lanark as a direct
   replacement for John Parke in November 1964, making his debut
   against his former side at Easter Road just days later in a 5-0 victory
   for the Easter Road side.

10 Under manager Jock Stein Hibs defeated Aberdeen in a third game
    play-off at Pittodrie in the final of that year's Summer Cup. The
    final was to have taken place at the end of the previous season but
    had been postponed until the start of the following season due to an
    outbreak of Typhoid in Aberdeen.

11 For the first time ever Hibs had defeated Rangers three times in
    domestic competitions in the same season. A 4-2 win at Ibrox in
    October was followed by 1-0 victory at Easter Road in the January
    in the league followed by a 2-1 home win in the quarter-final of the
    Scottish Cup in March.

12 Expected to be ready in time for an earlier game against Hamilton
    Academicals the covered enclosure or 'Cowshed' behind the bottom
    goal was finally opened in time for the New Years Day derby against
    Hearts in 1966.

13 At the start of the 1966–67 season the Scottish authorities had
    decided to allow the use of a substitute but only in the case of injury,
    and on 12 November 1966 Pat Quinn became Hibs first official
    substitute when he replaced the injured Joe Davis during Hibs' 5-1

defeat by Clyde at Shawfield.

14 Although not used, at the beginning of the 1966–67 season Jimmy O'Rourke had been listed on the team sheet as substitute for a League Cup game against Rangers at Ibrox. The previous year the SFA had eventually relaxed their ban on substitute goalkeepers being used for European games, and Thomson Allan who had yet to feature in the first team, became the first Hibs player to be stripped for action if needed in a competitive European match in the game against Valencia in Spain in October 1965.

18

15 The former Hibs goalkeeper Thomson Allan was capped against West Germany and Norway in 1974 while with Dundee. Although he was part of the Scotland squad that made its way to Germany for the World Cup Finals that year he remained unused. After a loan spell with Meadowbank Thistle he would sign for Hearts during the 1978–79 season.

16 Joining Newcastle United in 1967, Jim Scott would collect a Fairs Cup winners medal with the Tyneside team in 1969, the clubs first ever venture into European competition.

17 Rangers had suggested either Alec Smith or the future Manchester United manager Alex Ferguson in exchange as part of the Colin Stein deal but this was refused by the Hibs chairman William Harrower and the transfer went ahead on a strictly cash only basis. Ferguson would later move to Falkirk before ending his playing career at Ayr Unite and the rest as they say is history.

18 The Hibs goalkeeper Willie Wilson was known as the 'Man in Black' quite evidently because of his penchant for wearing an all black playing kit.

19 Hibs beat Manchester City for the signature of the Partick Thistle player Arthur Duncan in January 1970 reputedly paying £35,000 for his services Duncan making a goalscoring debut at Easter Road in a 2-1 defeat by Celtic. It would be money well spent, the player ending

his time at Easter Road with the most number of appearances by a Hibs player.

20 After only one substitute appearance the previous season, the 18-year-old John Brownlie would make his debut for Hibs in midfield against Dunfermline on 18 April 1970. However, he would quickly find his true position at right back and for a time would undoubtedly be the best full-back in the entire country. Although the Scotland side for the games against Denmark and Russia in 1971 had been depleted by injury, Brownlie's inclusion against Russia, while a surprise, was never the less even this early a tremendous testimony to the youngsters reputation.

19 PAT STANTON

1 After signing for Hibs Stanton would be farmed out to the Juniors, in his case Bonnyrigg Rose and would later relate that his time at Bonnyrigg would be the making of him as a player, learning to compete against older and more experienced players.

2 He made a goalscoring debut in Hibs 4-3 defeat by Motherwell at Fir Park On Saturday 5 October 1963. Hibs other goal scorers that afternoon were Gerry Baker and Neil Martin, the future Celtic and Hibs player Joe McBride scoring a hat-trick for the home side.

3 Stanton would make his full Scotland debut alongside team mate Jim Scott in a 3-0 defeat by Holland at Hampden on 11 May 1966. It would turn out to be Scott's only cap.

4 Stanton would be awarded his first full cap by the former Hearts and Ranger player John Prentice. Prentice had replaced Jock Stein only weeks before but would manage Scotland for only three months before being replaced by Malcolm McDonald, who himself would only be in the position for a couple of months before being replaced by the former Rangers goalkeeper Bobby Brown.

5 At the start of the 1969–70 season Stanton took over the Hibs captaincy from Joe Davis who would soon join Carlisle United, bringing to an end the quite remarkable record of 273 consecutive games for the club.

6 As well as Stanton, Hibs other goalscorers against Napoli that unforgettable evening at Easter Road were Bobby Duncan, his first ever for the club, Pat Quinn, Colin Stein and Peter Cormack.

7 He was voted the Scottish Football Writers Player of the Year, then a fairly rare occurrence for someone outside the 'Old Firm' to receive the honour.

8   Hibs first game on the way to League Cup success in 1972 was a 4-2 home victory against Queen's Park, the Hibs goal scorers that afternoon Johnny Hamilton (2 , Stanton and Alan Gordon.

9   In the days before extended injury time at the end of a game became the norm, the Hearts fans would later claim that Stanton's equalising goal in a 1-1 draw at Tynecastle, a full five minutes after the 90, was so long over-time that in the days when pubs opened at 5 o' clock for the evening session they were already drawing the first pints in Gorgie Road.

10 Stanton would claim that Hibs reserves were his second favourite team.

11 He was nicknamed 'Niddrie' by his Easter Road team mates after the area of Edinburgh he hailed from.

12 Jackie McNamara who would go on to give Hibs nine seasons loyal service before joining Morton in 1985.

13 Stanton's last ever appearance as a Hibs player was as a substitute during Hibs 9-2 home league cup victory against St Johnstone on Saturday 28 August 1976, replacing the injured George Stewart in the second half. Hibs goalscorers were MacLeod (2 , Brownlie (2 pens , Muir (2, Bremner, Duncan and Ally Scott.

14 By this time a Celtic player, his last ever appearance in a Scotland jersey was when selected along with the Aberdeen goalkeeper Bobby Clark as one of the two over-age players in an under-21 game against Czechoslovakia in 1977.

15 After over 40 games for Celtic during the 1976–77 season when he would win Scottish Cup and league championship medals, Stanton would manage only one appearance the following season in the opening league game against Dundee at Parkhead when he was forced to leave the field after an hour to be replaced by Johnny Doyle. He failed to fully recover from the injury and after almost

14 years as a professional it would prove to be the players last ever game.

16 After leaving Aberdeen, Stanton became manager of Cowdenbeath and later Dunfermline before taking over the Easter Road hot-seat in 1982.

17 His assistant was now his former team-mate John Blackley who himself would replace Stanton as manager of Hibs in 1984.

18 In November 1982 the cash strapped Easter Road club would pay Partick Thistle £60,000 for the services of the Scottish international goalkeeper Alan Rough and it would prove to be money well spent, Rough winning a further two Scotland caps during his almost six seasons in Edinburgh.

19 On Sunday 30 April 1978 Hibs played Celtic at Easter Road in a testimonial for the well respected Stanton, both sides fielding several guest players. Such was Stanton's reputation that despite the terrible weather over 20,000 attended the game.

20 sHe would make 16 appearances for Scotland, captaining the side three times in games against Russia in 1971 and Wales and Ireland in 1973, only injury preventing him from captaining the side against England at Wembley. As well as his appearance as an overage player against Czechoslovakia, he also made seven appearances for the Scottish League and three for the under-23 side.

19

20 TURNBULL'S TORNADOES

1   Turnbull replaced the former Manchester City player Dave Ewing in the summer of 1971.

2   The 14-year-old Craigroyston schoolboy Gordon Strachan was an s-signing when Turnbull joined the club in the summer of 1971 but he would not be long at Easter Road, supposedly after an argument between his father and the new Hibs manager, and he would soon join Dundee.

3   Eddie Turnbull's first game as manager was against English Second Division side Middlesbrough in a pre-season friendly at Easter Road on Saturday 31 July 1971, the visitors winning 2-0, both goals scored late in the game.

4   The former Dunfermline and Birmingham City goalkeeper Jim Herriot was signed from Durban City at the start of the 1971–72 season. Not yet registered with the football authorities Turnbull took a chance and played him in a friendly against York City at Bootham Crescent under an assumed name.

5   Although the result was immaterial Hibs Pat Stanton was in the Scotland side that defeated a Glasgow select 2-1 in a game that raised £45,000 for the disaster fund.

6   In November 1971 Alex Edwards was signed from Dunfermline making a goalscoring debut some weeks later in a 3-2 home victory against Kilmarnock. His first start had been delayed due to the fact that he was still serving a suspension when he signed for the Easter Road side which was strictly against the rules. Turnbull would later be severely censured by the authorities for his disregard for the rules.

7   Both the 1972 and the 1973 Drybrough Cup competitions were played under experimental rules that were designed to encourage more goals being scored. Now a player could only be offside inside a

20

line stretching from touchline to touchline 18 yards from goal.

8   Hibs were trailing 2-1 at the interval during a thrilling League Cup quarter final tie against Airdrie at Broomfield when right back John Brownlie scored twice the goals helping his side to a comprehensive 6-2 victory. Hibs would win the return game in Edinburgh 4-1.

9   The game against Ayr United, then managed by the former Hibs player Ally MacLeod, would end 8-1 in the home sides favour. During the game Alan Gordon would score a hat-trick his third goal Hibs 100th in all competitions since the season began.

10 After breaking his leg in the game against East Fife in January 1973, John Brownlie would be replaced in the side by the former Highland League player Des Bremner. After just over seven seasons at Easter Road Bremner would join Aston Villa, winning the European Cup with the midland club in 1982.

11 Under the direction of the Hibs fanatic and composer of the famous Z Cars theme Johnny Keating, in 1973 the Hibs players would record an 8" disc entitled 'Hibernian – give us a goal', the words written by Tom Hart's wife Sheila. The flip side was called 'Turnbull's Tornadoes.' Although never intended to top the charts, nevertheless it sold very well in Edinburgh and the surrounding area and if rumour is to be believed, the management team at EMI thought it the best football song that they had ever heard.

12 Despite a 4-2 home victory over the Yugoslavian side Hajduk Split in the third round of the Fairs Cup, a 3-0 defeat in Split would signal the end of Hibs European aspirations. Goalkeeper Jim Herriot was blamed for at least two of the goals and he would never play for the first team again.

13 With Jim McArthur injured and Roddy McKenzie, a recent acquisition from Airdrie ineligible, the former Rangers goalkeeper Bobby Robertson played in both legs of the Fairs Cup game against Keflavik. Robertson who had also made a substitute appearance in

Hibs away game against Hajduk Split the previous season would make only a handful of appearances for the first team before a return to Junior football at the end of the season.

14 In the opening game of the 1973 Drybrough Cup competition at Easter Road Hibs fielded Iain Munro a new signing from St Mirren against his former team mates. During the summer, goalkeeper Jim Herriot had joined St Mirren on a free transfer and he too would also be making a debut for his new side against his former team mates.

15 The 1973 Drybrough Cup Final against Celtic at Hampden was still goalless near the end of extra time with penalty kicks looming when Alan Gordon scored the only goal of the game in the very last minute after a pass from substitute Cropley to give Hibs the cup for a second consecutive season.

16 Against all expectations, Hibs first visit to Tynecastle after the comprehensive 7-0 victory on New Year's Day would end in a 4-1 defeat for the Easter Road side, Alex Cropley scoring the visitors solitary goal.

17 Concerned that football was becoming overexposed on TV, at the start of the 1974–75 season Tom Hart had banned the cameras from Easter Road before a League Cup game against Rangers, goals by Gordon, Duncan and Harper giving the home side a fairly comfortable 3-1 victory. He would also repeat his actions before Celtic's championship winning victory at Easter Road two years later.

18 In the game against Celtic at Parkhead in October 1975, Hibs were leading 2-0 when the referee abandoned the game with only a few minutes remaining. A heavy blanket of fog had made it impossible to continue. Earlier, after Harper had given Hibs a two goal lead, the home fans spilled onto the pitch, the game was held up for several minutes. Because of the circumstances the Easter Road side believed that they should have been awarded the points, only for the authorities, somewhat incredibly, to order that the game be replayed,

20

Erich Schaedler scoring one of his rare goals in a 1-1 draw in the replay.

19 A member of Hibs League Cup victory against Celtic in 1972, Alex Cropley would also win the League Cup with Aston Villa in 1976.

20 The former Aberdeen and Everton player Joe Harper scored all the goals in the 5-0 victory.

21 THE MANAGERS

1 Both Alex Maley of Hibs and Willie Maley of Celtic were brothers. The game between Celtic and Hibs was believed to have been the first time that brothers had opposed each other in a national cup final.

2 The Maley family had long connections with Celtic and many of the Hibs supporters were still resentful that in the early days the newly formed Celtic had taken many of Hibs best players, one of the reasons for the club temporarily going out of business in 1891.

3 The long serving former player Johnny Halligan, who replaced Bobby Templeton, was apparently a reluctant caretaker manager at Easter Road for a few months until the appointment of Willie McCartney in 1936.

4 Walter Winterbottom. Winterbottom was the first England coach/ manager, holding the position from 1946–62 before being replaced by the 1966 World Cup winning manager Alf Ramsey.

5 Shaw was followed in the Easter Road hot seat by the former Queens Park and Clyde player Walter Galbraith who had previously managed the English lower league sides Accrington Stanley, Bradford Park Avenue, New Brighton and Tranmere Rovers before joining Hibs in 1961.

6 Centre half John McNamee became Stein's first signing when he joined Hibs from Celtic on 18 April 1964, making his debut in Hibs 5-2 home victory against East Stirling. During his short time at Easter Road 'Big Mac', who had made his Celtic debut in direct opposition to Joe Baker in 1961, would become a great favourite of the Hibs fans.

7 Bob Shankly, brother of the Liverpool manager Bill Shankly, replaced Jock Stein in the Easter Road hot seat in 1965.

8   Previously manager of the East of Scotland sides Gala Fairydean, Eyemouth and Hawick Royal Albert, the former Hibs player Willie MacFarlane managed Stirling Albion before he took over at Easter Road.

9   In the Hampden dressing room after a 0-0 draw with Rangers in the 1971 Scottish Cup semi-final the Hibs manager Dave Ewing was overheard by a journalist telling his players that 'Rangers were rubbish and not a football team at all'. The following day the story was splashed over the back pages of the newspapers, obviously much to the fury of the Glasgow side and their followers.

10 During the penalty shoot-out at the end of Hibs UEFA Cup game with Leeds at Easter Road in November 1973 the Leeds manager Don Revie had remained on the field as the players were taking the penalties which was strictly against the rules. An immediate protest was made to the authorities in Switzerland and although Revie was found guilty of deliberately infringing the rules, incredibly Hibs were still forced to forfeit the bond of 500 Swiss francs required on receipt of the protest.

11 Eddie Turnbull was once quoted as telling the highly intelligent Alan Gordon: 'The trouble with you Gordon is that all your brains are in your f****** head.

12 Former player Bertie Auld led Hibs to the Second Division title in 1981 after replacing Willie Ormond who had been forced to resign for health reasons earlier in the season. Auld's assistant was the former Hibs player Pat Quinn.

13 Although not technically the manager, the former Celtic player and recently appointed development officer Billy McNeil would look after the first team affairs for a few weeks until the arrival of Alex McLeish.

14 Franck Sauzee, whose reign as manager at Easter Road unfortunately would be brief, a humiliating defeat by Second Division Ayr United

in a League Cup semi-final at Hampden signalling the beginning of the end of his time at Hibs.

15 Three. Matt Busby (wartime), Ally MacLeod and Willie Ormond. In 1978 Eddie Turnbull would spend a short time as assistant manager to Jock Stein.

16 Mixu Paatelainen in Hibs 6-2 victory at Easter Road in October 2000.

17 Previously a player, then assistant manager under Jim Jeffries at Tynecastle, Billy Brown would hold the same position at Easter Road under Colin Calderwood. After Calderwood's sacking in 2011 Brown would take over as caretaker manager for a few weeks until the arrival of Pat Fenlon.

18 Pat Fenlon joined Hibs from the Irish side Bohemians.

21

19 Fenlon's first game as the Hibs manager against Motherwell at Fir Park, was abandoned at half time after one of floodlights caught fire.

20 Eleven. Hugh Shaw, Willie MacFarlane, Eddie Turnbull, Willie Ormond, Bertie Auld, Pat Stanton, John Blackley, Franck Sauzee, John Collins, Mixu Paatelainan and John Hughes.

22 THE '80S

1   After several seasons with Clyde, Joe Ward joined Aston Villa during the 1978–79 season although he would play very few games at Villa Park before a move to Hibs as part of the Bremner transfer deal. Unfortunately he would struggle to hold down a regular first team place at Easter Road and would soon be transferred to Dundee United.

2   George Best's home debut against Partick Thistle on 1 December 1979, a 2-1 victory, would attract well over 20,000, many of them possibly just to see the charismatic Irishman in action. The attendance was more than three times the number that a game between the sides would normally have attracted at that time. The revenue from that one game would have gone some way in paying Best's reputed £2,000 per game, an astronomical sum at that time, during his entire time at Easter Road.

3   Eddie Turnbull's last game as manager of Hibs was the hugely embarrassing 5-0 defeat by Celtic in the Scottish Cup semi-final at Hampden on 12 April 1980. He would be relieved of his duties a few days later.

4   Willie Jamieson became Eddie Turnbull's last ever signing for the club when he joined Hibs from Tynecastle Boys Club. Turnbull would later relate that as both parties were about to sign the contract he looked down to see that Jamieson was actually wearing Rangers socks!

5   Somewhat bizarrely Alan Sneddon would win two league championship medals that same season, the Premier League with Celtic and the First Division title with Hibs.

6   Under manager Bertie Auld, Hibs would win the First Division championship with a 2-0 victory against nearest challengers Raith Rovers in the last home game of the season in 1981. The Hibs

goalscorers that day were Gary Murray and Ralph Callaghan.

7   During the 1981–82 season the highly rated 19-year-old Bermudian striker Ricky Hill would play several reserve games for Hibs as a trialist, one of the games against Hearts on a snow bound Easter Road pitch. Despite wearing several pairs of socks and a couple of t-shirts under his jersey the weather was obviously not to the youngsters liking and he returned home to Bermuda promising to return when the weather had improved. Scottish weather being what it is he would never be heard of again in Edinburgh.

8   In January 1981 the former Hereford defender Ian Hendry was carried off with a broken leg just 20 seconds into his debut against Berwick Rangers at Shielfield. On his recovery from the injury he would make just one more appearance as a substitute before signing for Nuneaton Burgh.

9   Joining Dundee as part of the exchange deal with striker Bobby Hutchison in 1977, left back Erich Schaedler made a return to the club in 1981.

10   Since the Second World War only 12 players have received a testimonial while at Easter Road. Incredibly, in 1983 five players on Hibs books at that time would later receive testimonial games, Jim McArthur, Alan Sneddon, Gordon Rae, Jackie McNamara and Arthur Duncan. Another, Gordon Hunter who was then a provisional signing would not feature in the first team that year.

11   During a 2-1 home defeat by Rangers in November 1985, the Ibrox player John McDonald, according to most unbiased bystanders, made a meal of a soft tackle by Ally Brazil to earn his side a penalty. The Hibs Chairman Tom Hart would later be fined £500 for his 'controversial comments' in a newspaper. Later, Erich Schaedler would be severely censured by the authorities after describing the Rangers player as his favourite actress in an article in the match programme.

12 The 8-1 home victory against Kilmarnock in April 1883 with goals from Thomson (2 Irvine (2 Duncan, Rae, McNamara and McCurdy.

13 Involved in an altercation with a linesman after a disputed decision during a home league game against St Johnstone in November 1983, the former Morton and Middlesbrough player Bobby Thomson would later be banned for six months. After serving the lengthy suspension, the following season he would struggle to regain a first team place and would join Blackpool after a short spell back at Cappielow.

14 During a league game at Ibrox in September 1984 the young Hibs fullback Kevin McKee was guarding his post at a corner when without warning he was attacked by a Rangers supporter who had entered the field of play. The attacker was immediately arrested by the police but the incident appeared to have a lasting effect on the player and some say that he was never the same again. After the incident he would make very few appearances for the first team at Easter Road and would join Hamilton not long after.

22

15 Gordon Durie, who would be transferred to Chelsea in 1996, later signing for Spurs and Rangers before a short spell with Hearts.

16 A very young John Collins would replace Ally Brazil in the second-half of the 3-0 defeat by Aberdeen at Hampden on 27 October 1985.

17 The Hibs goalkeeper Alan Rough would be the only one on both sides to escape a caution after the major altercation that followed Graeme Souness being sent-off for a horrendous tackle on George McCluskey, although the goalkeeper would be booked in a separate incident later in the game. At a later appeals tribunal, the bookings received by Mickey Weir, Mark Fulton and George McCluskey would all be rescinded.

18 The five players were Stuart Beedie and Billy Kirkwood who had both been signed from Dundee United, the former Celtic player

George McCluskey from Leeds, Willie Irvine from Stirling Albion and Mark Caughey from the Irish side Linfield.

19 Dougie Bell would be joined at Easter Road that day by Tommy McIntyre and Graham Mitchell, all three making their debut in the game at Brockville.

20 Signed from Coventry City for £325,000 the FA Cup winner Keith Houchen would delight the Hibs supporters when scoring on his debut against Hearts at Tynecastle with a spectacular header, although Hibs would ultimately lose 2-1.

23   FIRSTS

1   By defeating Dumbarton in the 1897 final Hibs became the first side from the East of Scotland to win the coveted trophy.

2   A 2-0 victory against Queens Park on 13 September 1924.

3   There were two. The former Linfield players William Gowdy and Jack Jones both played in Ireland's 3-2 victory against Wales at Belfast on 11 March 1936.

4   The former Bohemians player Pat Farrell played against both Switzerland and France in 1937. Farrell had also been capped for Northern Ireland against Wales in 1938. Players were allowed to play for both Eire and the full Ireland side until the early 1950s.

5   In 1937 loudspeakers were installed at the ground for the first time, now allowing announcements to be made over the air.

6   Willie Ormond scored his first goal for the club in a 1-1 draw with Rangers at Easter Road on 14 December 1946, a game even this early described by some as a possible championship decider.

23

7   The League Cup Final would be Jimmy Bradley's one and only appearance for the first team. Pitched into the side only because of injury to Turnbull, the youngster had been quite clearly overawed, had a poor game in the 3-0 defeat, and would soon be on his way to Third Lanark.

8   Lawrie Reilly's first hat-trick for the club was in a 6-0 home win against Queen of the South on 11 December 1947. Hibs other goal scorers that day were Ormond, Combe and Turnbull.

9   Under lights normally used only for training purposes with a few extra lamps added behind each goal, Hibs defeated Stenhousemuir 5-3 in a floodlight friendly at Ochilview in 1951.

10 With Reilly, Smith and Younger all delayed by fog at the airport after a Scottish representative game in Denmark, centre forward Jock Buchanan became the first British player to score a European Cup goal on home soil in the 1-1 draw with Rot Weiss Essen in the return leg at Easter Road on 12 October 1955.

11 Joe Baker's selection for the full England side now meant that Hibs had supplied players for all four of the home countries. James McGhee and James Lundie for Scotland in 1886, Bobby Atherton for Wales in 1899 and William Gowdy and Jack Jones for Ireland in 1936, not including Pat Farrell for Eire.

12 After a remarkable career spanning 18 seasons, on 1 November 1958 Gordon Smith, then recovering from a serious injury, made his first ever official appearance for the reserve side in a 2-2 home draw with Rangers. Pitched directly into the first team as a 16-year-old in 1941, technically Smith had occasionally played for the second team during the war years when the club had been short of players, but these games were classed as unofficial.

13 Smith was the first player to feature in the European Cup with three different sides, Hibs, Hearts and Dundee.

14 The former Hibs goalkeeper Lawrie Leslie, then with Airdrie, had been first choice for the game against England in 1961. However, he was recovering from injury leaving the unfortunate Haffey to carry the can for the embarrassing defeat.

15 George McNeill, who would sign for Morton after leaving Easter Road before deciding to retire from football to concentrate on professional athletics.

16 Hibs flight from Abbotsinch to face Sporting Lisbon in the Cup Winners Cup in 1972 was the very first time that the club had chartered its own aircraft for a European game.

17 Joe Harper in a 1-0 victory against Hearts at Easter Road on 30

August 1975.

18 At the start of season 1977–78 the Hibs players took the field wearing the logo of the sports manufacturer Bukta on their jerseys. In doing so they became the first senior football club in the entire country to wear sponsorship on their playing kit.

19 Sheila Rowland.

20 Hibs Scottish Cup tie against Stenhousemuir at Ochilview on 11 March 1995 was beamed back live to an audience at Murrayfield Ice Rink in Edinburgh. Hibs won the game 4-0.

23

24   THE DEVELOPMENT OF EASTER ROAD

1   During the 1949–50 season the main, or east terracing had been extended to cope with the huge post-war crowds that were then attending games at Easter Road, raising the capacity of the ground to around 70,000. Thankfully, with the crowd boom soon to be a thing of the past, further plans to raise the capacity to around 98,000 would be cancelled.

2   Hibs new Easter Road Railway Halt that was situated immediately behind the east terracing, was officially opened before a home game against Clyde on 8 April 1950 and would now allow visiting fans to arrive directly at the ground by rail although the return journey would be required to be made from the stations at Abbeyhill or Waverley. Originally extremely popular, the increasing number of cars and the improvement of roads would see a gradual reduction in its popularity and the scheme would be discontinued sometime around 1968.

3   One of the quaint provisions laid down by the Dean of Guilds was that the steel latticed towers should not display any form of advertising.

4   The well known Edinburgh engineering firm Miller and Stables labelled the system 'Drenchlighting.'

5   On 16 October 1954 Hearts defeated Hibs 2-0 in a game to officially inaugurate the new Easter Road lights. In 1957 Hibs would return the compliment at the opening of the Tynecastle lights.

6   In 1955 work on a new retaining wall near the player's entrance at Easter Road would mean the removal of the existing structure that housed the ornamental crest of a harp set into a three foot circular design painted green, white and gold. The crest was never replaced and to this day there are some who still look upon the development as having sinister overtones.

24

7   The construction of the new scoreboard at the south east corner of
     the ground was one of several changes that took place at the stadium
     in 1955. It replaced the somewhat archaic structure that had stood
     for many years at the north east corner before it was moved for a
     short spell to the rear of the south terracing.

8   During the club's pre-season trip to Holland in 1958, the Hibs
     directors had been impressed with the four inch line markings that
     were being used as opposed to the normal two and a half inches
     then in use by British Clubs. It was found that when the games at
     Wimbledon's centre court were televised that the lines were normally
     widened for the benefit of the TV cameras. At that time no machine
     existed in this country that was capable of laying the wider lines and
     one had to be specially imported from the continent, and although
     hardly one of national importance it is believed that Hibs were
     the very first club in Britain to use the wider lines that are now an
     accepted practice throughout the country.

9   Instead of Edinburgh council constructing a brand new stadium at
     Meadowbank to accommodate the 1970 Commonwealth Games,
     Harry Swan had suggested that the Easter Road pitch could be
     turned 90 degrees and the ground entirely covered. Unfortunately his
     innovative suggestion that the city could finance the entire project
     and lease the ground back to the club on match days was rejected
     and the white elephant at Meadowbank went ahead as planned.

10   Originally expected to be in use for the game against Hamilton
     Accies at the beginning of November, delays would mean that the
     covered enclosure was not officially opened until 1 January 1966 in
     time for the New Year's Day derby against Hearts.

11   The then PR man Tommy Younger had been appointed secretary
     of Hibs newly opened social club that was situated in the car park
     behind the main terracing. After its initial success, regular violence
     both inside and outside the premises would eventually ensure the
     club's premature closure.

12 In the summer of 1980 Hibs became the first Scottish football club
to install under soil heating. Originally utilising the use of electricity,
the system, which is now a prerequisite for all clubs playing in the
Premier League, now uses hot water pipes situated a few inches
below the surface.

13 Since 1893 the Easter Road ground had been leased, first from the
Trinity Hospital Trust and then the Edinburgh District Council, but
in the summer of 1981 the ground was purchased from the local
authorities and was now owned in its entirety by the football club.

14 During the late 1960s and early 1970s the game had been seriously
troubled by the problem of hooliganism and in 1974 Hibs became
the first football club in Scotland to erect security fencing around the
perimeter of the pitch in an effort to prevent field invasions by rival
fans. However, because of the tragedy at Hillsborough in 1989 when
96 supporters had lost their lives when the fences had prevented fans
from escaping the severe crushing on the terracing, the barriers at
Easter Road and elsewhere had been dismantled.

15 With crowds now nowhere near the numbers that had attended
games in the immediate post-war period, by the late '70s and early
'80s games inside a stadium designed to hold almost 70,000 were
often taking place before a tenth of that number and in 1983 the
huge terracing was reduced almost to its pre-war size, reducing the
maximum capacity of the ground to just over 23,000.

24

16 In 1985 an electronic scoreboard was erected on the roof of the
covered enclose at the north end of the ground. Intended to generate
extra revenue for the club, constantly beset by technical problems it
was not a success and would soon be dismantled.

17 The Taylor Report into the Hillsborough Disaster now required that
all stadiums over a certain size should be all seated by 1994. By August
bucket seats had been installed at Easter Road but because the south
end of ground lacked cover at that time visiting fans were provided
with free yellow plastic cagoules if the weather made it necessary.

18 Work on both the North and South stands took place during the 1995–96 season.

19 Wallace Mercer's attempt to take over the club in 1990 had highlighted the serious financial problems at Easter Road and it was initially felt that the club would be forced to move elsewhere. A new purpose built ground at Straiton was suggested, possibly sharing with Hearts, but thankfully the problems would eventually be overcome and the club remains at its spiritual home to this very day.

20 The famous Easter Road slope was levelled.

25 INTO THE '90S

1 As well as a member of the playing staff, the former Celtic and Borussia Dortmund player Murdo McLeod was also assistant manager to Alex Miller.

2 After the recent failed attempt to take over Hibs in 1990, the Hearts chairman Wallace Mercer was 'advised' by the police that in the interests of safety he should not attend the next game between the sides at Easter Road.

3 The nickname was earned after the club had come back from the brink of oblivion in 1990 to win the Skol Cup a little over 12 months later.

4 The future Everton and Manchester United manager David Moyes.

5 Wright scored in every round of that year's Skol Cup run on the way to the final.

6 As well as making 175 appearances for Hibs, Darren Jackson would also play for Scotland 20 times during his spell at Easter Road scoring three goals.

7 The future Northern Ireland manager Michael O'Neill, who joined Hibs from the Tannadice side in 1993.

8 Pat McGinley had been transferred to Celtic for £525,000 in July 1993 but just over a year later he would return to Easter Road for a then club record fee of £420,000.

9 Defender Gordon Hunter would score the only goal of the game at Tynecastle in August 1994, bringing a miserable run against their Edinburgh rivals to an end.

10 John Collins was in the Celtic side that defeated Hibs 3-1 in the cup replay after the first game had ended goalless.

25

11 Dow had actually been signed from Chelsea but at the time was on loan at Bradford City.

12 Previously assistant manager under Alex Miller, in 1996 the former Dundee player Jocky Scott would take over as caretaker manager between 30 August and 30 December that year until replaced by Jim Duffy.

13 Steven Tweed. The player's time in Greece however would not be particularly happy, managing just two games before returning to sign for Stoke City.

14 Jean Marc Adjovi Boco, known as 'Jimmy' Boco by the Hibs fans.

15 Chic Charnley, who would make almost 30 league appearances for the club between 1996 and 1998.

16 The former Keflavik goalkeeper Olafur 'Ollie' Gottskalsson would replace Jim Leighton at Easter Road. Later in the season Gottskalsson would temporarily lose his place, first to young Chris Reid then to the former Norwich player Bryan Gunn who was in goal when Hibs were relegated at the end of the campaign, but would regain the number one spot the following season with Hibs now in the First Division.

17 Manager Alex Miller's sons Graeme and Greg would both play a few games for the club during this time.

18 Jim Leighton captained Scotland in the games against Japan, Ecuador and the Faroe Islands, all in 1995. During the 1990s, six Hibs players were capped for Scotland at full level, Andy Goram, Darren Jackson, Jim Leighton, Murdo McLeod, John Collins and Keith Wright.

19 Fans favourite Franck Sauzee was knocked unconscious, losing four teeth, after a clash of heads with an opponent when scoring in Hibs 3-1 home victory against Hearts in March 2000. Hibs other goal

scorers that day were Latapy and Paatelainen.

20 Between January 1990 and December 2000 Hibs would play just
one UEFA Cup tie, against Anderlecht in September 1992. A 2-2
draw at home would be followed by a 1-1 draw away, the Belgian
side progressing into the next round courtesy of the away goals
ruling.

25

26 ARE ALL GOALKEEPERS CRAZY?

1   Disfigured after an accident with a cricket ball in his youth, it is said that the former Morton and Hearts custodian Harry Rennie, who would later coach the great Morton and Scotland goalkeeper Jimmy Cowan, was never the same goalkeeper after later surgery to repair the injury.

2   The Scottish international Willie Harper was transferred to Arsenal in 1925. The fee of around £4,000 which was then the record for a goalkeeper would have gone some way towards the cost of the new Easter Road grandstand.

3   Willie Robb, then of Rangers, would replace the injured Harper in Scotland's 3-0 victory against Wales in October 1925, and later in the Hibs side after the latter's transfer to Arsenal.

4   Signed from the Junior side Ormiston Primrose in 1938, the highly rated Jimmy Kerr would go on to give the club several years' service before a move to Queen of the South in 1952.

5   John 'Jock' Brown, father of the Scottish Rugby players Gordon and Peter, was himself later physiotherapist to the Scottish rugby team. Brown, a Scottish Cup winner with Clyde in 1939, was capped by Scotland against Wales in 1938 and was a registered Hibs player between 1942 and his transfer to Dundee in the late 1940s.

6   George Farm, later of Blackpool and Scotland.

7   Tommy Younger had spent much of his National Service stationed at a base in Germany but had been flown back to Scotland almost 80 times to take part in Hibs games. According to one of his former team mates the goalkeeper had a fairly easy time during his time in the army, often leaving on the Thursday for Saturday games he would usually not arrive back at his base until the Tuesday.

26

8   Signed from Junior football only at the beginning of the 1955–56 season, George Adams created history when he became the first ever British goalkeeper to feature in a home European Cup game. That season he would play 25 times for the reserves but would not play for the first team again and would be freed at the end of the season.

9   Willie Wilson in only his second appearance for the first team.

10 Baker had been joined in an England under-23 side by the then Hearts goalkeeper Gordon Marshall who had been born in Farnham. Unlike Baker however, Marshall would fail to progress into the full national side.

11 Ronnie Simpson. Simpson was also the youngest player to have taken part in a league game when playing for Third Lanark against Hibs in 1946, aged only 15.

12 After complaining of being blinded by the low Rugby Park floodlights during a game between Kilmarnock and Dunfermline, Herriot had been advised by his then manager Jock Stein to rub dirt on his cheekbones similar to the habit used by many American Football players that would help prevent the glare.

13 Herriot would eventually be replaced at Easter Road by Jim McArthur, who had been signed from Cowdenbeath during the 1972–73 season.

14 The former Airdrie goalkeeper Roddy McKenzie, who had been signed just days before, was in goals for Hibs that afternoon in what was considered a shock defeat after the result in Gorgie just months before. McKenzie however would play very few games while at Easter Road before a move to Clydebank.

15 In Scotland's World Cup Qualifier against Wales at Cardiff in September 1985 Hibs Alan Rough replaced Jim Leighton at half-time after the then Aberdeen goalkeeper Leighton claimed to have lost one of his contact lenses. It was immediately after this game that

the Scotland manager Jock Stein suffered his fatal heart attack.

16 In a home game against Morton in 1988 Andy Goram's huge kick-out from the edge of his penalty area completely deceived the opposition goalkeeper Wylie to land in the back of the net. Goram would also score one of Hibs goals in a penalty shoot out in a league cup tie with Clydebank in 1989.

17 The impressible John 'Budgie' Burridge' would win the Skol League Cup with the Easter Road side in 1991 to go along with the League Cup medal won with Aston Villa against Everton in 1975.

18 The former Hibs goalkeeper Andy Goram who had left Easter Road only at the beginning of the season to join the Ibrox club.

19 Bryan Gunn.

20 Andy McNeil. The current Hibs goalkeeping coach Alan Combe was in goals for Kilmarnock.

27 ODD FACTS

1 'Darling' Willie Groves who in the 1880s was one of Scotland's first ever superstars.

2 On 3 February 1910 a Scottish Cup reply between Hibs and Hearts at Easter Road was played during a heavy downpour of hail and snow that had threatened to obscure the lines from the start. Hibs had been leading 1-0 at half time, but because of the atrocious conditions, and the fans completely unaware of the decision, during the interval both sides had agreed to finish the game but that the result would stand as a friendly. Both clubs and the referee would later be fined for what was seen as a serious breach of the regulations.

3 Jimmy Dunn with Everton in 1933, and his son James with Wolverhampton Wanderers in 1949.

4 Busby was accompanied to the game against Celtic with his friend the great Stanley Mathews, who while interested in turning out for Hibs was stationed too far away to make it a practical proposition.

5 The attendance of 143,570 for the cup semi-final between Hibs and Rangers at Hampden is still a record for a game outside of a cup final or international match in British football.

6 During Hibs trip to Brazil in 1953 it is said that the Vasco de Gama officials had been so impressed by both Smith and Johnstone that they had been keen to sign both.

7 That afternoon at Ibrox, Preston was directly up against the famous Rangers and Scotland centre half Willie Woodburn. It would turn out to be Woodburn's last ever game. The following midweek the entire country would be stunned to learn that a disciplinary panel had banned the player for life after being sent-off during an altercation with a Stirling Albion player several weeks before. In

27

considering the facts the panel had apparently taken Woodburn's previously poor disciplinary record into consideration.

8   Lawrie Reilly in the 7-2 defeat in 1955, Johnny MacLeod in the 9-3 mauling in1961 and Arthur Duncan in the 5-1 defeat in 1975.

9   Although Hibs had been drawn against Lausanne in the first round of the Fairs Cup in 1960, the game would not take place after the Swiss side claimed to have been unable to raise a team. In the circumstances Hibs were awarded a walk-over and a 2-0 result.

10 Ronnie Simpson was just 15 when he made his league debut in 1945. Alex Edwards became the youngest outfield player to make his league debut just a few days after his 16th birthday in 1961, both against Hibs.

11 While training with Hearts in the evenings as a 16-year-old, Eric Stevenson had unknowingly signed a full professional contract which was then against the rules. When the situation eventually came to light manager Tommy Walker would be fined £150 and Hearts £75. With Hearts still unclear as to whether Stevenson was a free agent or not, Hibs wasted no time in stepping in to sign the now 17-year-old youngster, and he would go on to give the club many years of tremendous service.

12 The Norwegians Isaak Refvik and Sven Mathisen regarding a work permit.

13 Because of industrial action by electricity workers the game at Easter Road was played in the afternoon with a 1.30pm kick-off.

14 For several years UEFA had allowed the use of a substitute goalkeeper in competitive European games but only in the case of injury. Scotland however did not accept the ruling until the 1965–66 season, and Thomson Allan who was yet to play a first team game, became Hibs first official substitute in the away game against Valencia in October 1965 although not used.

15 John and Craig Paterson, Lewis and Andy Goram, Joe McBride senior and junior, Jimmy and Paul Kane, Alan and Mark McGraw and Gary and Simon Murray. Murdo McLeod's father, also named Murdo, played at least one wartime game for the club during the 1942–43 season.

16 Goalkeeper James Leighton and the Welsh international Leighton James.

17 Although the south terrace was still uncovered, to comply with the Taylor Report the stadium became all-seated in time for a pre-season friendly against Sheffield Wednesday on 7 August 1994.

18 The five Hibs players to have won the European Cup are Ronnie Simpson and Bertie Auld both with Celtic in 1967, George Best with Manchester United in 1968, Des Bremner with Aston Villa in 1982 and Franck Sauzee with Marseille in 1993 although by this time the competition had been renamed the Champions League.

19 Goalkeeper Mark Oxley scored one of the goals in Hibs 2-1 home win against Livingston in the first championship match of the season on 9 August 2014, when just 19 minutes into the game the bounce from Oxley's huge kick from his own area completely deceived the Livingston goalkeeper Jamieson.

20 They both had the names of famous American heavyweight boxing champions. Hibs, Ofir 'Rocky' Marciano, and Aberdeen Joe Lewis, although the Aberdeen goalkeepers name was spelt differently.

27

28 HANDS OFF HIBS

1 Kenny Waugh.

2 The venture capitalist David Rowland.

3 The former Morton player Neil Orr was bought from West Ham for £100,000 and goalkeeper Andy Goram from Oldham for £325,000 a few months later.

4 In 1989 Hibs became the first Scottish club, and only the second in Britain to be floated on the stock market.

5 Garry Dennis.

6 At a meeting in the Hibs supporters club later that evening the former Hibs director Kenny McLean was unanimously elected chairman of the fans led Hands off Hibs committee.

7 Alex Miller who had replaced John Blackley in 1986.

8 The Blue Peter presenter and Hibs fanatic John Leslie directly disobeyed his bosses by wearing the T-Shirt while on air.

9 The Talk of the Town nightclub was purchased by the club in December 1989.

10 Avon Inns, a chain of public houses and hotels in the Bath area that were bought a few months later. It would later turn out that both the Talk of the Town nightclub and Avon Inns had all been in receivership at the time and all owned by David Rowland.

11 They had both thought that the prospective new owner might be the newspaper magnate Robert Maxwell and had been absolutely stunned when who should walk into the room but the Hearts chairman Wallace Mercer wearing his club blazer.

12 Fearing trouble between the rival fans the police refused permission for a mass rally through the town.

13 The Hibs legend Joe Baker. The rally would end with a poignant rendition of 'You'll Never Walk Alone' by the Proclaimers.

14 It was suggested that if necessary Hibs could use the nearby council owned Meadowbank Stadium for their home games.

15 Despite being ordered not to attend the rally, the Hearts centre-forward John Robertson gave an inspiring speech in support of the Hands off Hibs campaign.

16 The Hands off Hibs 'Battle Bus' containing members of the protest committee made its way to Tynecastle to hand over a petition containing over 50,000 signatures opposing Mercer's plan. At the ground the committee would be received cordially, the feeling being that not everyone at Tynecastle approved of Mercer's plan to destroy the Easter Road club.

17 Brian Rogan and Tony Connor, two Hibs fans living in London handed over a copy of the petition at 10 Downing Street.

18 The former Hibs owner Kenny Waugh.

19 A new board fronted by Chairman Douglas Crombe included the former Hibs director Kenny McLean, Tom O'Malley, Allan Munro and Robert Huthersall. There would be no place for Duff, Gray or Rowland.

20 John Collins would soon be sold to Celtic for a fee said to be around £1,000,000.

29   MISCELLANEOUS

1   It would be the last ever game played at the first Easter Road. Although an attempt would be made to carry on playing at several different locations including Hawkhill, the club would soon temporarily go out of business. It would be reformed in 1893, now playing at the present Easter Road.

2   He became a debenture shareholder in the early 1920s when finance was needed to develop the stadium.

3   At that time Jock Govan was Scotland's regular right back and had played in the 3-0 victory against France in May 1948. However, Govan was ill at the time of Scotland's next game against Wales a few months later and his team mate Hugh Howie who was normally a centre-half would take Govan's place in the Scotland team. It was fairly unusual at that time for two players from the same side to occupy the same position in the international team.

4   On 22 October 1952 Hibs played Arsenal in a floodlit challenge match at Highbury to raise funds for the National Playing Fields Association. Billed as an unofficial 'Champions of Britain' match, Arsenal, who would go on to win the league that season, murdered a full strength Hibs side 7-1, Lawrie Reilly scoring the visitors solitary goal. The entire second half was broadcast live on TV throughout the country, but perhaps thankfully relatively few people at that time would have owned a television set.

5   Hibs reputation at that time had spread well beyond these shores and in 1953 they were invited to take part in an eight team competition comprising of sides from Uruguay, Holland, Scotland and Brazil. Although failing to win a game, drawing one and losing two, they made such an impression that a football encyclopaedia in the late 1960s would credit the club as having played a major part in the advancement of the game in that country.

6   The first game to be beamed live on TV from Easter Road was the
    last 30 minutes of Hibs friendly match against Manchester City on
    Monday 1 November 1955. Over 18,000 were said to have watched
    the home side defeat a City team that included the former Famous
    Five player Bobby Johnstone 2-1.

7   The world's first ever official penalty kick was scored by Renton's
    Scottish international James McCall on 22 August 1891 in a league
    match against Leith Athletic at Leith's home ground Bank Park
    which was situated just a few hundred yards from Hibs new Easter
    Road ground. Leith themselves would later miss a penalty in the
    same game. Royal Albert laid claim to the record when scoring
    against Airdrie in the Airdrie Charity Cup some weeks earlier
    but this had been before the new ruling officially came into use.
    Incredibly, in the early days players had to claim for a penalty before
    a referee could award it. The kick itself could be taken anywhere
    on a line drawn 12 yards from goal, the goalkeepe not allowed to
    advance more than six yards from the goal line. The first penalty in
    a league game in England was scored by Wolverhampton Wanderers
    against Accrington on 14 September the same year.

8   Lawrie Reilly with 18, Gordon Smith 17 although seven had been
    scored in what was classed as unofficial wartime games and Joe
    Baker 14.

9   The former Motherwell and Scotland player Pat Quinn, who would
    spend six seasons with the club until moving to East Fife in 1969.
    Quinn would later manage the Methil side before a return to Easter
    Road as assistant manager to Bertie Auld in the early 1980s.

10 Right back John Fraser was the Hibs captain that momentous
    evening, Peter Cormack the scorer of Hibs first goal in the 2-0
    victory. Fraser would later relate that he had been surprised to be
    spat on by his immediate opponent Gento.

11 Willie Hamilton had been given the afternoon off but insisted on
    playing after learning that a silver salver was to be presented to

the man-of-the-match. It turned out to be no contest, Hamilton easily winning the award by scoring seven consecutive goals in Hibs eventual 15-1 victory.

29

12 Just days after making his debut in Hibs 5-0 home victory against his former side Third Lanark on 14 November 1964, Joe Davis would go down with appendicitis. Incredibly he would miss just three games returning in time for a 2-1 home victory against Partick Thistle on 19 December, the first of an incredible 273 consecutive games for the club.

13 Peter Cormack. Cormack would spend over four seasons as a player at Liverpool during the 1970s after a spell with Nottingham Forest before joining Bristol City in 1976. He would return to Easter Road in 1979, first as a player then as assistant manager under Alex Miller.

14 For the first time two substitutes could now be used in competitive domestic games instead of the one as before, in Hibs case Tony Higgins and Jimmy O'Rourke, although neither would be used.

15 Captain for the day George Best's last game for the club was a 2-0 home win against Falkirk on Saturday 11 October 1980 wearing the number 11 shirt. Reputedly on £2,000 per game at Easter Road which was an astronomical figure for a Scottish side at that time, he would join San José Earthquakes at the end of the 1979–80 season. He made a brief return to Easter Road during the American clubs close season tour, returning to America immediately after the Falkirk game but would later return to Easter Road once more to take part in Jackie McNamara's testimonial.

16 Hibs were managed by Eddie Turnbull and Hearts by Willie Ormond. The English sides taking part were Manchester City and Coventry City, the latter taking the eye by wearing a dark chocolate coloured strip.

17 After seven seasons with Hearts, full-back Chris Shevlane had been

forced to retire prematurely because of injury but a few months later felt well enough to return to football and was signed by Celtic. However, at Parkhead he would make only four appearances before joining Hibs during the 1968–69 season.

18   Baker would wear the number nine jersey in all the games he started during his two spells with the club, except technically, when although he had been listed on the team sheet at centre forward, he had swopped jerseys with number 8 Bobby Kinloch in the return Fairs Cup game against Roma in 1961. In his second time at the club he had been substitute on a couple of occasions and would have then have worn the number 12 jersey.

19   Three points for a win would now replace the two as before.

20   Pat Stanton who made 399 league appearances for the club between 1963 and 1976 scoring 50 goals.

30 ALMOST THE STORY SO FAR

1 In 2005 Hibs travelled to Germany to play Rot Weiss in the Georg Melches Stadium in Essen to commemorate 50 years since both sides entry into the inaugural European Cup in 1955. Hibs won the game 3-0.

2 Paul Dalglish, son of the more famous Kenny who won three European Cups with the Annfield side. Dalglish junior would play just 13 league games for Hibs scoring once. His last goal coming in the away leg of the Inter Toto Cup against Odense in April 2006.

3 'Benji' made his debut for the club in Hibs ill-fated 4-0 defeat by rivals Hearts in the semi-final of the Scottish Cup at Hampden.

4 Lewis Stevenson made his debut in a CIS Cup tie against Ayr United at Somerset Park on 21 September 2006, Hibs winning 2-1. His league debut would come in a home game against Aberdeen on the first day of the following season, a 1-1 draw.

5 After Mowbray's departure his assistant Mark Venus elected to remain at Easter Road until a new manager was in place before rejoining his former boss at the Hawthorns.

6 They were both born in Hartlepool.

7 Rob Jones, Benjelloun (2) and Fletcher (2).

8 The former Newcastle United player Brian Kerr who was signed from Motherwell in 2007.

9 From a position just inside his opponents half, John Rankin's shot, later described by the player as a 'squiggler', dipped, completely deceiving the Celtic and Poland goalkeeper Artur Boruc for Hibs opening goal.

10 Then a registered Arsenal player, Stokes had a productive loan spell at Falkirk during the 2006–07 season scoring 14 league goals from just 16 starts. Sunderland would later pay £2 million for his services but before his first spell at Easter Road in 2009 he had been out on loan at both Sheffield United and Crystal Palace.

11 In a pulsating game at Fir Park watched by the TV cameras, Hibs had been leading 4-1 at one stage and later 6-2, when the roof caved in. Motherwell who had scored a tremendous equaliser in the 3rd minute of extra time to make the score 6-6 had even missed a penalty with the score at 6-5. At the time it was the highest scoring match in Premier League history. The Hibs goalscorers were: Nish (3) Stokes (2) and Riordan.

12 Stubbs started his playing career at Bolton Wanderers in 1990. He became Celtic's record signing in 1996 before two spells with Everton with a very brief stay at Sunderland in between. He would end his playing days with Derby County in 2008.

13 Substitute Darren McGregor in Hibs 2-0 victory over Raith Rovers at Starks Park on 9 January 2016. Dominique Malonga was Hibs other goal scorer that afternoon.

14 Lewis Stevenson who won both with Hibs, and John McGinn who was part of the successful St Mirren side that defeated Hearts 3-2 in the 2013 League Cup Final.

15 Signed by Hearts as a youngster, Gray was soon snapped up by Manchester United, playing one game for the Old Trafford side against Crewe Alexandria. Several loan periods would follow before signing for Stevenage. At the time of his signing at Easter Road he had been on a short term contract with Burton Albion.

16 An easy one. What was significant about Hibs game in 21 May 2016?

17 As well as a Scottish Cup medal with Hibs, the former Aberdeen

player Fraser Fyvie was also an FA Cup winner with Wigan, although as an unused substitute, in the 1-0 victory over Manchester City in 2013.

18 The Norwegian born Gunnarsson was also eligible to play for Sweden because of his father's birthright. His father Ronnie has an impressive pedigree in football. As well as being a licensed FIFA and UEFA match agent, he is also a columnist for a Swedish football magazine and has coached sides in Sweden, Norway and the Faroe Islands.

30

19 On Hibs run to the 2016 final, Cummings scored two goals, both against Hearts in the third round, one in the replay at Easter Road.

20 Leicester City.

31   DEFINITELY THE LAST WORD

1   Seven. Goalkeeper Conrad Logan, Fraser Fyvie, Jason Cummings, James Keating's, Niklas Gunnarsson, Chris Dagnall and Anthony Stokes, although Stokes would rejoin the club for the third time a few weeks later.

2   Hibs very first goal of the 2017–18 season was scored by Danny Swanston in a 4-0 victory against Dunfermline in a pre-season friendly in Fife on 6 July. The first competitive goal was scored by Simon Murray in a 4-0 victory against Montrose in the Betfred Cup at Easter Road on 15 July.

3   Previously with Bournemouth and Burnley, Marvin joined Hibs from Leighton Orient.

4   Signed from St Johnstone where he had been on loan from Coventry City, Swanston would make just eight league appearances for Hearts before a return to MacDiarmid Park, joining Hibs at the beginning of the 2017–18 season.

5   Hibs largest home crowd of the season was the 20,193 in a 2-2 draw with Celtic on Sunday 10 December 2017.

6   The registered Manchester City player Brandon Barker.

7   Hibs failed to score in just four league games during the 2017–18 season. Twice against Aberdeen, once at Pittodrie and again at Easter Road, Hearts in a 0-0 draw at Tynecastle and Celtic in a 1-0 defeat by Celtic at Parkhead.

8   McGinn made his full Scotland debut in a 1-0 victory over Denmark at Hampden on 29 March 2016.

9   Just two, Florian Kamberi in the 3-1 win against Hamilton Academicals at the beginning of April and Jamie Maclaren in the

31

5-5 home draw with Rangers on the final day of the season. Simon Murray also scored a hat-trick in Hibs 6-1 victory over Arbroath in July but that was in the Betfred League Cup.

10 Five. Marciano, Laidlaw, Cammy Bell who took over after Marciano had been sent off in the 1-1 draw with St Johnstone at MacDiarmid Park in March and listed from the start for the following home game against Partick Thistle. Maciej Dabrowski would make fourteen appearances as a substitute but would not be called upon, while Scott Bain on loan from Dundee was substitute against both Hearts and Celtic before his loan deal with the latter.

11 Shaw was a youth player at Hearts before signing for Hibs in 2015, making his first team debut as a substitute when replacing Alex Harris in the 3-0 home league cup victory over Montrose in August 2015.

12 Signed from Belgian side Mechelen in January 2018, the former Hearts player managed just one appearance as a substitute when replacing Darren McGregor during a 2-1 home victory over Motherwell in 31 January.

13 The most number of goals scored by Hibs in a single game was the six against Arbroath in the Betfred Cup. Five were scored on three occasions, against Ayr United in the Betfred Cup in August, Kilmarnock in the league in April, and Rangers on the last day of the season, all the games played at home.

14 Then playing for Leicester City in a game against Newcastle United at Filbert Street on 29 April 1998, the Newcastle and England centre forward Alan Shearer was accused of kicking the Leicester player on the head, deliberately according to some, accidentally according to others. No action was taken by the referee at the time but at a later disciplinary hearing Shearer would eventually be found not guilty. Lennon, to his great credit had appeared as a witness for the Newcastle player saying that as far as he was concerned the matter had been at an end immediately after the game.

15 Steven Whittaker who left to join Rangers in 2007 before rejoining the club in 2017, Scott Allan who left to join Celtic 2015 and was signed on loan from the Parkhead side in 2018 and Anthony Stokes who would sign for the club for a third time in August 2017.

16 Replacing Allan Stubbs on 8 June 2016, Neil Lennon's first game as Hibs manager was 1-1 draw at Berwick in a pre-season friendly on 5 July. His first competitive game was a 2-1 away win in the Premier League against Falkirk on 6 August.

17 Israel.

18 After topping a league cup group also containing Arbroath, Ross County and Montrose, a 3-2 home victory against Livingston would be followed by a 4-2 defeat at Hampden by Celtic in the semi-final.

19 Efe Ambrose with 45, including one as a substitute, scoring 3 goals. Lewis Stevenson was next with 44 and 3 goals. Both John McGinn and Martin Boyle would make 43 appearances, each scoring 6 goals.

20 Celtic's 3-0 victory over Motherwell in the Scottish Cup final assured fourth placed Hibs a place in the following season's European competition.

31

Some other books published by **Luath Press**

Hibernian: The Life and Times of a Famous Football Club
Tom Wright
ISBN 978 1912147205 | PBK £14.99

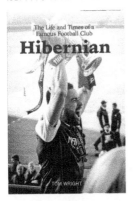

Hibernian Football Club, founded by a group of Edinburgh-based Irishmen and Irish descendents, was born in the Cowgate area of the city in 1875. A team of the people, its long history, heritage and rise to fame has created a tradition and influence that helped shape the game as we know it today.

In *Hibernian: The Life and Times of a Famous Football Club*, Tom Wright looks at Edinburgh's Hibernian Football club from its birth in 1875 to the present day. An anecdotal and personal journey, this volume highlights the many challenges, and lows and highs experienced by the team and its dedicated fans over the last 142 years; exploring the events that shaped the club from both World Wars, Hibs' 'Famous Five' days, the European Cup and the Scottish Cup win in 2016.

Hibernian: From Joe Baker to Turnbull's Tornadoes
Tom Wright

ISBN 978 1908873 09 1 HBK £20

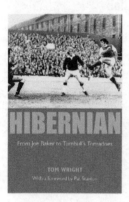

In *Hibernian: From Joe Baker to Turnbull's Tornadoes*, club historian Tom Wright marks a new dawn for the game and the end of an era for Hibs.

Hibernian begins in the turbulent 1960s, when relegation was avoided at Easter Road on the final day of the 1963 season.

The appointment of the legendary manager Jock Stein in 1964 saw an immediate improvement in the relegation haunted side. The Hibs side of the mid-'60s featured an all-Scottish international forward line, and the return of player Eddie Turnbull in 1971 saw the emergence of possibly Hibs' greatest-ever side – the magical Turnbull's Tornadoes.

Packed full of detail and interesting information, Hibernian is a must not only for Hibs supporters, but also for the general football fan who is interested in this defining period in the history of our game.

Hibs Through and Through:
The Eric Stevenson Story
Tom Wright

ISBN 978 1910745670 1 PBK £12.99

On 21 May this year, Hibs made history by winning the Scottish Cup for the first time since 1902. It was a time of celebration when the supporters revelled in their victory and remembered the great heroes of the club.

Eric Stevenson is one of those great heroes.

When he was inducted into the Hibs Hall of Fame at Easter Road in 2012, Stevenson declared, 'This means everything to me. My uncle founded the Bonnyrigg Hibs supporters club in 1949–50 and I started going to games when I was seven'. This book traces Stevenson's fanatical interest in the club from a very young age, his time as a left-winger wearing the number eleven green and white jersey in the '60s, and the well-deserved recognition that he has gained today.

Throughout his career, Stevenson also played for Hearts and Ayr United, but this story shows that ultimately he is truly *Hibs Through and Through*.

The Alex Cropley Story
Alex Cropley with Tom Wright

ISBN 978 1 910745 73 1 PBK £9.99

Signed to Hibernian aged just 16, Alex Cropley soon made his name as one of the legendary Turnbull's Tornadoes. In the 1970s he played for Hibernian, Arsenal, Aston Villa, Newcastle United, Toronto Blizzard and Portsmouth, before injuries forced him off the pitch. From football-mad kid playing on the streets of Edinburgh to member of the Scottish national team, his career epitomises both the aspirations and the bitter disappointments surrounding the game.

Crops is a testament to the passion of generations for the beautiful game. Updated to include Cropley's most up-to-date thoughts on Aston Villa having been relegated from the Premier League, and peppered with anecdotes about the footballing legends Cropley played alongside – this new edition of Crops is a must-have for any football fan.

With his educated left foot, Alex was a tremendous talent, but I have to say he could also be a real pain in the neck. A nippy sweetie, he was always moaning, but that is often the sign of a great player – a real determination to succeed and a refusal to settle for second best. – From the Afterword by PAT STANTON

Details of these and other books published by Luath Press can be found at:
www.luath.co.uk

Luath Press Limited

committed to publishing well written books worth reading

LUATH PRESS takes its name from Robert Burns, whose little collie Luath (*Gael.*, swift or nimble) tripped up Jean Armour at a wedding and gave him the chance to speak to the woman who was to be his wife and the abiding love of his life. Burns called one of the 'Twa Dogs' Luath after Cuchullin's hunting dog in Ossian's *Fingal*. Luath Press was established in 1981 in the heart of Burns country, and is now based a few steps up the road from Burns' first lodgings on Edinburgh's Royal Mile. Luath offers you distinctive writing with a hint of unexpected pleasures.

Most bookshops in the UK, the US, Canada, Australia, New Zealand and parts of Europe, either carry our books in stock or can order them for you. To order direct from us, please send a £sterling cheque, postal order, international money order or your credit card details (number, address of cardholder and expiry date to us at the address below. Please add post and packing as follows: UK – £1.00 per delivery address; overseas surface mail – £2.50 per delivery address; overseas airmail – £3.50 for the first book to each delivery address, plus £1.00 for each additional book by airmail to the same address. If your order is a gift, we will happily enclose your card or message at no extra charge.

Luath Press Limited
543/2 Castlehill
The Royal Mile
Edinburgh EH1 2ND
Scotland
Telephone: +44 (0 131 225 4326 (24 hours
Email: sales@luath. co.uk
Website: www. luath.co.uk